THE TWO FACES OF LEE HARVEY OSWALD

A TALE OF DECEPTION, BETRAYAL AND MURDER

BY GLENN B FLEMING

First published in 2003

EMPIRE PUBLICATIONS
1 Newton Street, Manchester M1 1HW

ISBN 1 901 746 37 2

Cover photographs courtesy of the author.
Cover design and layout: Ashley Shaw & Glenn B Fleming
Edited by: Ashley Shaw

Printed in Great Britain by
Ashford Colour Press,
Gosport, Hants.

For Joanne

In memory of Hazel Hale
and William Bobo

Contents

About The Author

Glenn B Fleming was born in Manchester, England and has spent the last thirty years researching this book.

In 1973, a chance encounter with a magazine article and several conversations led him to begin research into the assassination of President John F Kennedy. Though the trail was by then ten years old, Fleming's meticulous research led him to conclude that Lee Harvey Oswald had not played any part in the actual shooting of JFK but may, incredibly, have been infiltrating the group that were planning the murder.

Since publishing a series of articles in the magazine *Undercover* in 1993, Fleming has remained silent, although his research continued. The result is *The Two Faces of Lee Harvey Oswald* - a stunning trip through perhaps the most famous crime of the twentieth century through the eyes of John F. Kennedy's alleged assassin.

Foreword

Although researching and writing this book has been an intensely private, frustrating yet uplifting effort throughout many, many years, a great number of people have crossed my path brandishing their own brand of wisdom and humour.

'Forget it,' they laughed. Then, 'How do you know?' followed by, ' Yeah, yeah, I knew that all along.'- there have been only a mere handful who listened and still fewer who thought I might just have something to say.

Those people know who they are and I thank them for their support. Ruth and my family must also take a bow for just being there, especially my late father, who could never quite fathom how I managed to get so involved.

Glenn B Fleming

Acknowledgements

Special thanks go to Ashley Shaw for his help on the manuscript, my publisher, John Ireland, for his encouragement and support throughout and Andrew Clarke for his enthusiasm.

“We are opposed to apartheid and all forms of human oppression. Our concern is the right of all men to equal protection under the law.”

JOHN FITZGERALD KENNEDY

Preface

Heart pounding against his ribcage, a tidal wave of anxiety covered Lee Oswald as he ran toward the rooming house. He slowed to scan the area behind him - there were no cars travelling either way along the road, nothing moving toward him that he should worry about - but worry he did. Oak Cliff was usually quiet at this time of day, he knew that, but today was different. He'd felt out of breath since the short jog from the taxi that had dropped him at the northwest corner of the intersection of North Beckley and Neely, just a few hundred yards from his room. He was out of shape, that much was obvious, and his fitness was something he'd always prided himself on: he normally felt he could run all day if he needed to. But today, when he felt he may have to run all day, he knew he couldn't.

...Del Gado would roast me alive in hog fat if he see me now, puffing and wheezing...

It must have been 70 degrees on the sidewalk and seemed to be getting hotter by the second. The road merged into a heat haze half a mile away; the shimmering lamposts, buildings and sky blended into one fuzzy image, reminding him of distant drunken nights with his Marine buddies in the Philippines. His legs wouldn't carry him fast enough to the room and he felt vulnerable partly because he had left his .38 in his room that morning but mainly because he was no longer in control of the situation around him. He'd never felt so... open to harm.

Apart from when he was in the service, he had never carried a firearm with him and had never wanted to - until now. For almost three years in the Soviet Union he'd felt so confident that things would work out that he never carried a weapon. And things had worked out there in the end, hadn't they?

For the most part he consoled himself that for all the intrusions and bother from the local NKVD or whomever those guys had been, he'd always felt somehow protected. Safe. But now, back in the country of his birth, among so many people he knew, some he even trusted, a hundred yards from the relative safety of his room, Lee felt uneasy.

Is Ruby around? Where the hell is Ruby …

He turned and saw the red roof of his rooming house.

…damn sumbitch…

Oswald spat, cursing the thought.

…I'll get you, you bastard - someone ought to fix you, somebody soon - somebody will…

As he jogged, he considered going straight to Ruby's apartment less than a mile away.

…nah…too obvious…wouldn't be there anyway… I need my revolver … I have to stick with the plan …that cop should be here soon … what did Ruby say? "Go on home after the job. One of our guys will pick you up from there. I'll see you at Redbird airport around two. Don't fuck this up, Oswald. Don't fuck this up!" Well, fuck you, Ruby - you fucked up…

Oswald felt sick to the stomach and scared right down to the very depths of his soul. More scared now than... ever before.

… I need to change …

His T-shirt was stuck to his back and it was dirty from his morning's work.

…God, I need a shower, won't have time…

He was almost there. A thought crossed his mind...

What will the housekeeper think of my turning up in the middle of the afternoon…

He dismissed it. It wasn't important. He needed the

revolver much more than he needed to explain to her why he wasn't at work. He felt deep into his pocket for his key. He pulled it out and clasped it in his hand as he ran down the path, the door growing larger in front of him.

... she never locks the door anyway ...

The key returned to his trouser pocket as he moved to the mesh door and pulled it open. Holding the mesh with one hand he wrestled the door handle with the other.

...she'll hear the noise but fuck it... no time to wait around. I'm in and out and gone...

The door pushed open effortlessly - it wasn't locked. He moved through the mezzanine and into the hall, the lounge was at his left and he could hear the television booming. He stopped for a second, framed in the doorless entrance to the lounge. Mrs Roberts was there, a handkerchief close to her cheek, some guy wailing on TV. Lee watched her for a long second. He wanted to ask her the question, but dare not. His eyes shot from the TV screen to the back of her head. Everytime he looked at her, the question zapped from his eyes like a laser beam and hit the back of her head. Still, controlling his breath, his chest rising and falling, his heart strong and obvious, he made no sound.

Suddenly, Earlene Roberts turned and stood in one movement, facing him. The handkerchief stayed where it was. Her large glasses usually hid her eyes well, but now they were wide with disbelief, touched by horror. Her jowley face seemed to shake as she saw him, as if a cold shudder had gone down her spine. Lee stared at her, his face betraying a similar confusion.

'Oh, Mister Lee!' She blurted. 'Someone shot at the president'

Lee grunted as he moved to his right away from the outburst and to his room, the first along the corridor. No time for conversations. No time for questions. No time, even, for answers. He almost pushed the door off its hinges as he made for his dresser, stood at the right of the room, past the foot of his bed. The door bounced back behind him and he lunged for the bottom right dresser drawer. He pulled it open and felt his way through his work shirts. Then Lee felt the cold metal of the revolver - lying there, waiting. He pulled it out, snapped it open and checked the drum to see if it was loaded. He knew it was, but still needed to be sure. He felt the six shiny, round, brass Remington-Peters .38 Special bullets housed snugly in their chambers. Waiting.

Lee dropped the gun onto the bed and reached into the drawer again, pulling out a box of cartridges. In his haste, he spilled them into the drawer. Rescuing four or five bullets, he pushed them deep into his pocket. He pulled off his plaid overshirt, then the soiled off-white T-shirt almost in one movement and threw them onto the bed next to the revolver, reaching for another T-shirt from the open drawer. Pulling it quickly over his head and sticky body, he reached for the overshirt he'd just removed - though he knew it was hot out there, he also knew that any flight from Redbird in Ferrie's Piper Cherokee would be a chilly affair, not to mention the cold Texan nights ahead. He felt sick again at the thought of flying with Ferrie and Ruby.

Then, he quickly straightened his T-shirt and put his overshirt back on. Casting a swift backward glance to the bedroom door, he picked up the revolver and shoved the gun into the front waistband of his pants, before fastening the overshirt to the chest to cover the gun. He could hear the noise from the TV but couldn't make out what was being said. Then another noise pervaded his dizziness. He heard the sharp tit tit of a car horn, directly outside the house. Lee moved to the window and pulled back the curtain lace. Opposite the front lawn was a Dallas police patrol car. Oswald thought he could make out two uniformed officers in the car.

...two of them...

His mind raced.

...Ruby said 'one of our guys'...

The vehicle wasn't quite stationary, moving ever so slowly along the street. Then it speeded up and moved out of his sight.

...what's going on...

Lee moved swiftly back into the hallway, through the bedroom door that he'd stupidly left open. He could hear a reporter talking on the TV set but couldn't grasp the meaning of the words. Earlene Roberts was looking out the window too. She frowned and let the curtain back.

'You sure are in a hurry...' Her words followed him through the door and he was gone.

Part One
Incarceration

1

'Jesus,' Oswald muttered to himself.

'Keep your fucking mouth shut, cop killer,' spat the police officer to his right as he clutched Oswald's face in a vice-like grip - knuckles white with pressure.

'Maybe we should fix this guy right now, Tom. What do you think?'

'Love to. Just give me one good reason and I'll blow this sonofabitch's head off.'

Lee Oswald stared ahead; eyes fixed on the driver in front.

The car sped on.

Turning corners at high speed, sirens wailing, only feet, sometimes barely inches, from the lead car. Oswald heard the tyres screech as the driver, thankfully, failed to turn the car over.

Lee's wrists were manacled behind his back. He was almost sitting on his hands. He could do nothing to prevent the occasional blow to his face or body that the cops would level at him. He felt tired and longed to rub his sore face, but could not.

One of the police called through to headquarters. He heard them report that they were headed east on Jefferson with a suspect in a cop slaying.

The static coming back over the two-way obscured most of what was said by headquarters and Lee was not familiar with the jargon anyhow. With the two policemen sat either side of him talking at each other and sometimes screaming at him, Lee saw little point in trying to listen to half garbled messages over the radio.

He sat further back into the seat and closed his eyes.

Suddenly he was hungry, then just as quickly Lee felt violently sick. He desperately wanted to throw up all over the car and these bastard police officers who had violated him so much. Instead, Oswald just took several silent deep breaths. If he'd shown any signs of doing anything, anything at all, it would have only resulted in more blows raining down upon him. The arresting officers seemed convinced that Oswald was trying to escape from them even now and he was sure that he wouldn't enjoy being ejected from the car, however fast it may have been moving.

...but what of the plan? The 'impossible-to-go-wrong' plan that Bishop told me about? The plan that was so watertight that it couldn't possibly fail, even if it had wanted to? What of it? It had gone wrong. Something, or someone, had messed up...

A nudge disturbed Lee's thinking, followed by a booming, unfriendly voice.

'You still in there? Don't think you can dream yourself out of this one, buddy, 'cos you ain't goin' no place.'

...asshole...

Lee opened his eyes.

The dullness in his skull was quickly turning into a thunderstorm.

'Where are you taking me?' Lee said quietly, turning to one of his captors, 'What have I done to...'

'Just keep your mouth shut, boy, you'll get to know all you need to know in due time.'

'But, I've done nothing. You must have the wrong guy...' Lee dropped his head. It was painful to even try and talk. His jaw ached and he searched his mouth for loose teeth with his tongue.

'Well, boy, ain't that the truth. If y'all done nothin', then I guess you got nothin' to worry about.' The detective spoke with venom, as the two men looked each other squarely in the eye.

'But if you've done what we think you've done, then you're in big, big trouble, my friend.'

The detective grinned slyly, as if he knew something that Lee didn't. Then he sat back in his seat and stared ahead. Lee continued to stare at him for a few seconds longer. The detective must have been about thirty, only a few years older than himself. Oswald began to wonder if this man was like this at home, if he had a home at all. Or maybe it was the job he was in. No wonder people disliked the police so much, especially if they treated other people in the same manner as he'd been this afternoon, never mind the fact that they may have been innocent. As he was.

...and yet, I'm not as innocent in all this as I'm trying to make out. But a cop killer? That's what the detective in front said over the radio...

The radio squawked again and Lee couldn't help straining to hear its semi-coded message.

'Two.'

The officer in front picked up the microphone and held it to his mouth.

'Two, go ahead.'

'Two, suggest you take route five on returning suspect to home, over.'

'Home this is two, copy you on that. Looks like we got us a good one, over.'

The detective looked over his shoulder at Oswald, his dead pan features revealing no feeling. Lee looked away, trying to look disinterested. The detective faced forward again.

'Two, this is home, out.'

The radio crackled and went dead. The detective put down the microphone and looked back at Oswald.

'You got anything you wanna say, fella?' he said, 'Anything at all?'

The detective glared at Oswald but Lee held his gaze.

You are an empty, lifeless shell...

He fixed the vibes between them with contempt. A long, slow grin appeared on the policeman's face but even that could not hide his cold, hard, expressionless features. Lee held the stare for as long as he could, then glanced away. Nothing he could do here would change this man's problem. Things were bad, that was evident. Lee would not let the thought that things were as bad as they could be settle.

...if these police think I've had anything to do with Dealy Plaza...

Oswald stopped himself asking about the condition of the President. He remembered when he'd entered his rooming house on North Beckley; his landlady had been watching television.

'Oh, Mister Lee! Someone has shot at the President?' she had said... just what had she meant by that? Was the President dead or just wounded? That was something too big to deal with right now and Lee figured that there was enough on his plate as it was. Maybe Kennedy hadn't been hit at all...

A feeling of unease slowly settled upon him as he tried to get some perspective on events. No amount of training could perceive actualities. Whilst in the marines, Lee had often wondered what combat was really like and, on the odd occasion, he had practically yearned for it.

Oswald remembered Nelson DelGado, his sergeant, almost wetting himself one day on the shooting range. Lee had fired a full clip and two hand-loaded rounds and missed the target. Not missed the top score, but had missed the target itself. Lee's embarrassment had only been avoided later that month when he beat all of his comrades, including DelGado, in their first Russian language test. After all, Lee knew he and his unit were never going to see action, even if there were a war in the near future. Intelligence was to be the name of the game for Oswald and his buddies. Intelligence gathering and evaluation. It didn't matter one damn thing whether he could shoot straight or not, nor did it matter whether he knew which end of a rifle was which. No ordinary marine was he. No, sir. Smart cookie is Lee Harvey Oswald.

*

So just where the hell am I now?

In a cell, with green walls.

Lee exhaled loudly, but stopped abruptly as his lungs began to hurt. The sharpness of the pain took away what little breath he had left.

Thankfully, after he'd been booked, the detectives had allowed him to be handcuffed with his hands in front. At least he could take a pee, he thought, glancing at the john in the corner. And, thank God, he was alone. That should give him time enough to think his way out of this mess.

Slowly, deliberately, Oswald pressed his hands against his ribs as he searched for anything that may need a doctor.

... nothing broken ... but just what are those bastards waiting for? They can't possibly have anything on me ... a cop killer? What cop?

The only cops he'd seen that day were outside the Book Depository, those that had just tried to beat him to a pulp inside and outside the theater and the one who gave him the lift.

Something was wrong though and he dare not let the thought prevail that all this was connected with the President.

...No, it's deeper than that. Bishop wouldn't be too far behind me now. He might already be upstairs speaking to the Chief, clearing me of any involvement in absolutely anything that has happened today, especially a cop slaying... no, give it a couple of hours and I'll be out of here, gone... back to Marina and back to New Orleans. A new start with the money waiting from this little caper. A new place to live, probably a whole new identity, our very own home. No more leaning on other people like the Paines. Or my brother or mother for that matter...

Love him as they might, Oswald's relations certainly

figured that if they were going to help him and his family through these difficult times they were going to call all the tunes and no mistake.

It was the same as New Orleans, back in the summer. Start a fuss, get arrested, booked and the local FBI man would be down to sort it out.

...then I'll be free. Then I'll walk. Walk right back to New Orleans, money in my billfold, Marina holding my hand, Junie by my side and Rachael in my arms...

His very own family. Nobody to depend on, no one to rely on. Just him and his three girls.

...yeah...

For a split second that thought made him feel better.

Much, much better.

Lee dropped his head and felt the utter frustration of the situation. It was worse than that and he knew it. This was a big deal, not a scuffle with some jumped up Cuban in a street nobody had heard of. This was serious. And he couldn't help wondering if he were the only one of the group in jail.

...but for killing a cop? I never killed no cop. I never killed anybody. It doesn't make sense...

Oswald slowly stretched out on the bunk as he let his mind wander back to the theater.

2

Lee stood on the corner of Jefferson and Zangs, waiting for Billy. He'd walked to the corner from the police car that had dropped him off midway between Jefferson and Davis.

The police officer driving, who he was sure he'd seen someplace a few weeks before, was to take him to Red Bird airstrip, just a couple of miles south-west of his rooming house.

Lee was alarmed to discover that this plan had fallen through and that now he was to meet with Billy in the Texas Theater on West Jefferson. Oswald's first inclination was to proceed the few blocks east to Marsalis Street and Ruby's apartment, but considering the situation he let that idea fall. The cop was quite adamant about the change in plan and refused to answer any of Oswald's questions.

'Look, buddy,' said the patrolman, moving away from the kerb even before Oswald had closed the car door, 'that's all I have for you. You gotta go to the Texas Theater. Why? I don't know. I only hope you do, that's all. You think I care?'

The cop seemed somewhat perturbed by Oswald's presence. Lee eyed him cautiously. Could the cop have any idea about what had happened in the Plaza? Oswald noted that the car radio was off.

...maybe the guy is off duty, but I don't believe that... maybe he's a bogus cop... whatever... he seems ...scared. But of what?

'If you wanna get out of the car here, there you go. I got my orders. I give you a lift. Where to?'

Oswald looked at the patrolman, who stared ahead at the road.

After a long pause, Lee said, 'Just follow your plan, buddy. Let's just get there in one piece and we'll all be fine.'

Lee Oswald sat back into his seat. He didn't like changes in plans. To replace one thought with another in a situation like this could be fatal. The police car headed south on Beckley. The police officer did not engage Oswald in small talk. Oswald sank further back into his seat.

...make this ride last forever... make it last a million years and more...

Lee felt tired and the easy roll of the vehicle calmed him somewhat and he slowly rubbed his face. The car cruised on down Beckley, past Neely Street.

The cop leant over and switched on his radio.

A sharp blast of static disturbed Oswald's quiet demeanor.

Lee held his breath as the officer picked up the microphone and began to speak - Oswald eyed him curiously.

...what is he going to tell dispatch? That he had arrested a suspect in the shooting of the President? He couldn't be...

The police officer couldn't know whether Oswald was armed or not, surely he wouldn't take that chance. The cop glanced at his watch. The Dallas police dispatcher cut into the murmur of traffic clogging up the radio.

'Oak Cliff, go ahead.'

This was it, anticipated Oswald. Lee slowly brought his right hand up to his waist. The driver could not see this action, nor did he seem to be expecting it. Lee looked at him. The cop was too damn cool, he thought.

' ...am approaching Beckley and Tenth ...'

That's not our present position ... Beckley and Tenth is a block over to the east ...

The officer continued. 'Do you have anything for me, over?'

'Oak Cliff, be at large for any emergency that comes in, over.'

The patrolman threw a glance at Oswald then looked away. 'Copy, Oak Cliff. Out.' He replaced the microphone.

Oswald could contain himself no longer, 'What the hell is all that about?' he inquired.

The cop looked at him, then back at the road ahead.

'Beats me. Get that sort of thing all the time. Nothing usually comes of it though.'

'Sounded pretty serious. How do you work that kind of thing out?'

'Well,' said the cop, 'you just do. I mean, you can't dwell on it too much, even if something does come of it.'

The patrol car turned right onto the Davis intersection and then left onto Zangs Boulevard. The car quickened as the police officer pressed the gas. Oswald waited for the Eighth street sign. Seconds after the car had passed it, he spoke.

'Here,' said Oswald abruptly. 'This will be fine.'

'Whatever you say, buddy, whatever you say.'

The police car slowed to a halt, midway between the intersections of Davis and Jefferson. Oswald opened the door and got out. Neither he nor the officer spoke. Lee pondered the cop's role in the day's events. After a few seconds, he concluded that he might have been involved but rather doubted it. This kind of activity must go on all the time. Informers, stoolies must get rides in police cars all the time.

As Lee walked away from his ride, he heard the radio burst into life again.

'All cars, all cars, be on the look out for a white male, approximately thirty years old ...'. The police car sped off down Zangs. Oswald watched it turn left and head east on Jefferson. Lee concluded that the officer was heading to the location that he'd mentioned to the dispatcher moments ago.

Oswald continued south, following the police car's route, down Zangs to the intersection.

The Texas Theater is only minutes away ...

Oswald snapped out of his reverie. Outside the cell along the corridor but out of Oswald's sight, there came the distinct sound of movement, scuffling, fighting. Someone else, a drunk by the sound of things, was being led to a cell.

Lee got up from the bunk swiftly and grimaced as the pain shot through his ribcage. Moving on with teeth clenched, hands to his chest, Lee peered through the bars. Left, then right.

Pushing his face up to the cold metal, he heard curses from different sources filling the air. The outcries were silenced with the shattering clang of metal on metal as the cell door was closed. Then, that awful twisting of the keys rattling in the lock, more metal on metal drifting aimlessly down the corridor toward him, echoing in the stillness. The sounds flowed through the bars, into his cell, into his soul.

Footsteps walked away into the distance and Oswald returned to his bed. Lee's mind again returned to the corner of Jefferson and Zangs.

3

...Any news from downtown is evidently taking its time to reach this quiet suburb ...damn - doesn't anyone have a radio or TV on in this place? Someone must have some news from Dealy Plaza by now ... they must know the condition of the President, presuming that he's been hit ...

Oswald slowly, reluctantly, let that thought wash over him. He began to breathe more deeply, the warm afternoon beating down on him as never before. Wiping his brow, Lee scanned the area around him.

To his right was Jefferson Boulevard and the old Library building, one of those early so-called masterpieces dating from the previous century. Its red bricks reminded him of the old Court House building in Dealy Plaza, just a block or so south east of the Book Depository. The Court House stood out like a sore thumb, much the same as this Library did.

Turning to his left, Oswald had a perfect view of Jefferson as it angled away at forty-five degrees.

Anything heading his way would be noticeable to him in seconds. The buildings were low, nothing higher than the gas station sign hanging twenty feet in the air. He stared at the sign as it creaked occasionally in the mild breeze.

...God, what wouldn't I give to be in a cool shower right now...

Oswald could almost feel the cooling water pouring over his body as he closed his eyes, washing away the morning's grime from the Depository and the terrifying thoughts in his head.

And Marina?

His lovely Marina joining him in the aqueous coolness, feeling her tender caresses and her his. For a few scant seconds, Lee Oswald made silent love to his wife, something they'd not managed in weeks. He became angry as Marina's last words to him the evening before fell squarely on his tortured peace.

"We must leave Ruth's soon, Lee."

Marina had whispered to him as Ruth Paine had gone into the kitchen to make them all coffee.

"Ruth is the kindest person I know here - she has helped us a great deal. But we must move soon," she continued.

Lee had nodded slowly in agreement, shame and frustration.

... *how can I tell Marina what I'm up to in Dallas? How dangerous it is for me, for us all? How can I explain that I could get better work with better pay back in New Orleans or that there's four thousand dollars in cash in a post office box at the bus station near the apartment we lived in on Magazine Street...*

Lee recalled how often he'd been close to tears. Then he remembered how many times those same tears had fallen as he pined for his wife and young family during sleepless nights in his lonely room on North Beckley. This thinking was not relieving his situation.

Lee pulled himself together and focused on the present. Shops, stores and the occasional diner littered the long straight Jefferson Boulevard, crossed only by various intersections of roads and railway lines.

Oswald hated this area of Dallas. He hated those who lived here and despised the county's brashness. Abhorred vehemently the entire Oak Cliff section of the State.

...why don't those rich, smug oil millionaires and billionaires living over on the nice side of town put some of their spare cash into providing jobs for the poor and needy, living, no surviving, in this

area...

Hearing a car backfire sent more chills through his slender frame, jogging the thought of attempted assassination back into his confused head.

...those people shooting at the President were the best around. They must have hit Kennedy. Damn, what the hell could have gone wrong ...everybody would have been in position and I told Bishop almost the exact layout the group had discussed at the meetings in Mexico City. Who was here, who was there... what the hell had happened...

Lee tried as hard as he could to get some positive thoughts into his confusion, but to no avail. His mind wouldn't, couldn't stop racing through a myriad of negative impulses, over and over. He began walking to the Texas Theater. At first he moved briskly toward the supposed haven just over fifty yards away. Cursing aloud, Lee berated himself for his eagerness, convinced that someone may identify him later. Slowing down and glancing all around at the same time, he concentrated on the job ahead.

...just keep moving... nice and easy...

As long as he walked toward the Theater at normal pace no one would suspect him of anything. Wearing his paranoia on his sleeve had become something of a trademark since those early days in the Soviet Union. Part of the art of not being stopped over there had been to look like you expected to be checked. After another glance about the street ahead, memories of cold days in Moscow and Minsk disappeared like breath in the wind. Not only was there nobody observing his seemingly innocent actions in a poor suburb of a city somewhere a million miles from the oppression of the Soviet Union, there wasn't anybody walking these streets in any case.

Moving from the corner was like hearing the starter pistol on sports day at school. The sharp crack was instantly followed by a rush of blood to the limbs fuelled by adrenaline, then the breath sticking in the throat only to be superceded by the expectancy of the crowd. Oswald's blood pressure was doing a whole lot better than any hundred-meter athlete right now, but it was an ordeal all the same.

Lee put his right hand into his shirt, just above the waist.

There, warmed by his body heat and feeling smooth against his skin, his .38 caliber Smith & Wesson revolver nestled passive and inert.

Oswald wanted to pull the revolver from its sanctuary and check that it was fully loaded. He knew that it was of course but to remove it now would be nothing short of suicide. Pulling his hand from under his plaid colored shirt; Lee fixed his sight on the theater and what was going to happen in the next few minutes.

Knowing that he would be back in the lion's den gave Lee another odd feeling.

Of all the emotions he'd touched this fateful day, this was the most horrifying. Oswald had had no contact with the group nor Bishop for the best part of a week. He'd encountered no-one connected with the hit on the President that morning at the Book Depository and now he was on his way to meet with at least one of them in the darkness and seclusion of a semi-public place.

Trying not to let the thought of his role with the FBI and his relationship within the group, not to mention the day's events, invade his mind, Lee again fondled his revolver. Try as he might to keep his mind clear, one thought did break through his mental screen.

If it came to it, would he able to shoot Billy, or anyone with him, if they had rumbled him?

Beads of perspiration broke on Oswald's brow and he managed to suppress the urge to run and take his chances later, when he knew they'd come looking for him.

Lee was now less than seventy feet from his immediate future when all hell broke loose.

Incarceration

Police sirens shattered the still afternoon air, one police vehicle followed quickly by another screamed around the corner one block over from Beckley. Stopping dead in his tracks and spinning to his right, Lee looked into a shop window. Lots and lots of shoes filled his vision, the kind of shoes that Marina had pored over in one of Ruth's magazines. This thought and others passed quickly through his head.

Oswald's breathing quickened and he thought his heart would burst from his chest.

Through the window of the shop Lee thought he saw the movement of people rushing about. He instantly dismissed it as reaction to the chaos on his side of the plate glass. Oswald could feel sweat trickling down his back and stomach beneath his shirt. Getting hotter by the second Oswald held his breath as more police cars screeched around the corner from Zangs.

...what the hell is going on...

One squad car stopped abruptly behind him, tires screeching on the tarmac road, its siren whining down as if its life breath were being squeezed from it.

Staring into the reflection on the glass, Oswald saw the two officers sat in the front of the vehicle. The driver was busy talking on the radio as his colleague pulled a shotgun from its rest on the dashboard.

Oswald took a sharp breath as the officer pulled the barrel. Lee imagined he heard the snap and click as a round was pushed into the chamber.

He swallowed hard.

...a shotgun blast from this range...

The police car stayed motionless for what seemed like an age. The officer with the shotgun had opened his door and was in the process of leaving the vehicle when his colleague, still speaking into the radio, reached over and pulled him back into the car.

Oswald narrowed his eyes as he tried to fathom what words were being exchanged between the two men. As he concentrated on the car behind him, Oswald failed to see the store manager on the opposite side of the glass approach him cautiously. The store manager was taking a good long look at the man staring into his shop window. He had correctly observed that the police were trailing someone and he believed it was the man currently staring in the window.

The police car behind Oswald suddenly roared off west down Jefferson, its rear tires throwing up small stones and gravel from the road surface. Oswald could smell the gas fumes from the car's exhaust as it shot down the Boulevard, its siren again bursting into life. Another patrol car chased it, its siren also wailing.

Several people had collected on the corner of Bishop Street and were being questioned by another officer.

Lee exhaled heavily, thankful for a moment's respite but still not daring to move. Then he noticed the movement in the shop on the other side of the glass. Oswald saw the store manager watching him closely.

Their eyes locked for a second and Lee's instinct now was to run but he dare not. To his left were three other patrol cars and two at his right. Although they were many yards from his position, Lee knew that any movement he made would draw their attention to him and, he presumed, they couldn't see him from where they were parked. Their voices could be heard but only barely above the squawking of their car radios.

The immediate area was in chaos and more and more people were coming out onto the streets from their places of work.

Oswald remembered the man in front of him, re-focused his vision to the inside of the shoe store. The man had gone. Lee considered going into the shop, telling the man who he was and what was going on, but he knew he'd never believe him.

The police car that had stopped so abruptly in front of Oswald was now a hundred yards away. Lee turned his head slightly to his left and saw its tail-lights flash on as the driver applied the brakes. Almost in the same movement, the car swung around to the left, the driver performing a perfect U-turn. Had the car not turned away, the patrol vehicle at its rear would have smashed into it. Then the second car also completed a U-turn and both cars were now headed back up the boulevard, back toward Lee, by now standing frozen in the doorway.

Panic set in and Oswald's right hand moved slowly up to his shirt and the revolver.

...Christ the last thing I need right now is to kill some cop...

Oswald's clammy hand and fingers touched the opening in his shirt where the revolver was hidden. More sweat appeared on Lee's head and above his top lip. His breathing became more erratic and labored as the police cars drew closer.

As the lead car was level with Oswald, his hand rested firmly on the .38, the gun suddenly felt very different. Right now, Lee new exactly what this gun could do to someone and it passed his mind that somebody had designed it for that reason.

Lee was beginning to shake but his gun hand remained calm. He had the odd feeling of being a spectator in what was about to follow. As if it were not he these policemen were looking for, as if it were not he who now had the power of life and death in his hand. A nasty taste formed in his mouth and Oswald found it difficult to swallow.

Almost drowning in anticipation, Lee began to turn toward the street, steeling himself for his next action.

A picture of his family glazed over his eyes and he saw baby Rachael in Marina's arms.

How will they react when they are told of my death? How will they react when they are told that I've been shot down? How will they react when they are told that I've killed a Dallas police officer?

Still, the police patrol cars did not stop. He couldn't believe it. They drove right on past him; east on Jefferson then sharp left back onto Zangs. All of them.

As he turned to watch them go, Lee stepped further away from the window so he could observe the street.

As he reached the edge of the kerb all the police cars had started their engines and sped away. Oswald dropped his hand from his shirt, turned and began to walk briskly toward the theater, now just fifty yards away. The skin on his face was as tight as a mask, all the way from his jaw-line to the top of his skull. Any tighter and Lee was certain that it would rip. He passed an elderly couple who were clutching each other, obviously shocked and upset by the commotion.

'You ever known such a thing?' said the women to her man, who had his arm protectively around his her. The old man said nothing as Lee passed them. The police sirens wailed on into the distance and soon were lost in the Texan afternoon. As Oswald approached the theater, the patrons were stood looking toward Zangs, speculating as to what the commotion might be.

Oswald saw his chance. He walked up to and past them, he did so casually, looking over his shoulder in the direction of the fast vanishing police vehicles. Entering the theater, Lee could smell the dank aroma of cigarettes, mingled with the stale, still air. Moving into the semi-gloom, Lee walked past the ticket booth positioned to the left of the foyer doors and heard a movement to his right. He stopped.

An elderly Negro was sat reading a newspaper behind the concession stand. Oswald saw the ice cream and popcorn machines. Below them and in front were myriad candy and chocolate bars. The man shuffled his paper. Lee could hear no sound from outside, no sirens, not even conversations from the patrons talking outside the theater. As he reached the door to the foyer, he nipped quietly in. Glancing round as he headed for the double doors to the main area, Lee increased his step.

The darkness of the main floor enveloped Oswald as the door silently closed behind him. The air was cool and he began to feel the sweat running down his back, stopping only at the waist band of his trousers. He shuddered and felt the revolver thrust in his pants. Suddenly the .38 was a hindrance to him and he wished he could be rid of it, though Lee knew now that it was at this point that he might need the revolver most.

The support picture had just started as if someone had waited for Lee to enter. He allowed himself a tight grin. Someone was definitely waiting for him in the theater, but it had nothing to do with any film. Only maybe that person wasn't alone. The theater was all but empty. Oswald counted ten or maybe twelve heads scattered around the main floor.

Only two people were sat together that he could see. Straining his eyes to locate Billy, if he was there, Oswald slowly moved along the back row of the center aisle. He sat down midway between both aisles. The music roared from the film: the soundtrack mixed with the sound of cannon firing. Lee glanced up at the screen as the titles came up.

'Cry Of Battle'

The glare from the movie lent an eerie light to the main floor of the theater. Lee could see around him much better now, but still could not put his eyes on Billy. He settled back into the uncomfortable chair and tried to think out a plan in his spinning head.

Lee thought of putting his gun under one of the seats and leaving the building, taking his chances outside in the broad daylight, but dismissed the idea when he remembered Billy and his cronies would only come looking for him later.

No, he had to sweat it out. He must follow the plan so the group didn't suspect his FBI role.

Anyhow, if they had succeeded in murdering the president, surely they wouldn't be looking too hard for an informer among their ranks...

Of that he was sure. If the President were dead and they'd all got away, he could pick up his blood money and disappear. Lee horrified himself when he began to even contemplate the President's death in the hope that the group wouldn't need to search for the person who upset their plans.

The thought sickened him to the core. He felt more and more depressed as the seconds ticked by. Rubbing his face to relieve its tightness, Lee stared blankly at the screen. The actor Van Heflin and his troops were charging an enemy machine gun post, firing into it. The audience could see the killing, hear the shooting, screaming, shouting, cursing, falling, dying.

Oswald began looking around the main floor before him again. His eyes darted to every head in the place, from one to the other, over and over.

...Billy must be here...

Lee's eyes dropped to the two men sat eight or nine rows directly in front of him. His heart leapt to his mouth. It was Billy... or was it? Even with the light from the film it was still too dark to see them clearly, the light was projected in front of them, leaving their bodies in silhouette.

Narrowing his eyes and stretching his neck and head forward toward the two men, Oswald slowly wetted his lips. He felt dry and his tongue seemed shriveled inside his mouth. Unconsciously, Oswald's right hand moved into his shirt, searching for his revolver.

... if it is them, they haven't seen me. Maybe I could fix them both now and explain to the cops...

Lee sat back and took his hand out of his shirt.

... stupid idea. Damn stupid idea ...

As Oswald meditated on his dilemma, he failed to notice

the house lights brightening. Lee was in another world, one where he could just get up and go home to Marina and the kids and get the hell back to New Orleans or maybe California or some damn place away from all this.

His eyes had drifted in a subconscious way; away from the two men back up to the screen. Lee couldn't hear the sound now, such was his concentration on the situation. Oswald blankly observed a man walk out onto the stage in front of the screen, followed by several police officers. Then he suddenly and distressingly realized why he hadn't been hearing the sound track these past few seconds. The picture was silent. As this dawned on him, the screen went blank altogether and the house lights came up.

Cold chills ran the length of Oswald's spine.

The man on the stage appeared to be pointing straight at him. Oswald recognized the man as being the person in the shoe store who had watched him as the police cars did their fine work on Jefferson. The police stood on the stage were following the line of the man's arm.

They were looking directly at him, there was no doubt about that. Oswald glanced about him. To his right and left he saw the exit signs, dimly lit in the front corners of the theater adjacent to the stage. A cop barred the way in each.

If Oswald chose to run, the only place would be down the aisle, a sharp right and back out the front entrance.

Simple as this may have been, Lee knew that that action could cost him a whole lot more than he wanted to pay right now. He stared ahead, frozen to his seat and watched as the police officers, uniformed and plain clothed, moved down from the stage and begin to mingle with the people sitting before him.

A heavy silence hung in the air. One detective to Oswald's right motioned for a woman sat in the front row to stand. The woman did so and Oswald wondered if she were as frightened as he. The Officer checked her bag, but all the while kept Oswald in his sight. He couldn't have been more obvious about it. The woman, bewildered and tense, resumed her seat and stared rigidly ahead.

Another movement to Oswald's front right averted his gaze. Another detective had moved up the aisle toward him. Lee lowered his head but kept his eyes firmly on the approaching policeman. He held his breath, clenching his teeth behind closed lips. Again his right hand moved closer to his shirt and the .38 now felt as large as a howitzer and just as heavy.

Then, to Oswald's astonishment, the policeman turned to his right and began to move down the aisle toward the two men sat in front of Lee. The two men stood and raised their hands as the officer came to them. Lee saw the sides of their faces for a second and they looked bewildered and confused but no more than any ordinary person would when confronted by a cop frisking them for no apparent reason. Oswald strained his ears as one of the men said something to the detective. Lee couldn't catch the conversation, but saw the detective's mouth move in answer. The plainclothes officer searched his companion before telling them both to be seated. Oswald still couldn't see who they were and then could only see the backs of their heads and shoulders again as they sat down.

The detective didn't look at Lee as he moved back down the row of seats toward the aisle. Oswald's eyes followed him all the way though, even a slight movement from the officer to his left went unchecked as his gaze impaled the detective like a spear.

As the detective reached the row of seats occupied solely by Oswald, he stopped abruptly.

'On your feet.' He barked, startling Oswald, who instinctively pulled his hand away from his weapon. Oswald stood straight up, faced the policeman, raising both hands in the air, Oswald couldn't believe it. The detective was smoking a large cigar. Lee hadn't noticed it previously, but now he could smell the lingering odor from it.

... *smells like hell* ...

Oswald had dismissed the matter in less than a second. The detective looked angry and determined as he moved slowly toward Lee.

Oswald spun his head around, taking in the full situation. All the members of the public were sat back in their seats except the two men in front of him, but he still couldn't identify them. Now the detective was within a couple of feet of him.

Lee's thoughts were jarred as the detective put his hands onto his waist, searching for a hidden weapon.

Oswald, for the first time that day, panicked. In a voice barely louder than a whisper and to no-one in general, he blurted, 'Well, it's all over now.'

The detective's head was at about Lee's chest level. Oswald looked down at him. The policeman looked up, his cigar smoke getting in his eyes. Lee looked down, contemptuously. The detective's hands were moving fast and getting closer to the revolver.

Oswald had about a second to react. Moving slightly away from the officer he shouted, as loud as his terrified lungs would allow him, 'I am not resisting arrest, I am not resisting arrest–'

The detective flung himself at Oswald; his body weight aimed at Lee's abdomen. The two men fell down into the seats. Amid curses and groans, Oswald felt an armrest dig into his back, a sharp pain cleared his head. He now had his hands around the officer's neck while the detective began hitting him and hollering at the same time.

Lee looked ahead, the ceiling whirling as the policeman pulled him up and then pushed him further down into the seats again.

'I am–', was all Lee managed to get out this time, the

officer's hand falling across Lee's mouth like a clamp. Lee turned his mouth and head away as fists began to reign down on him.

'I am not … resisting arrest! If … if they shoot me, you're all witnesses!'

Oswald managed to get the words out. His determination to speak seemed only to increase the detective's determination to overpower him. Oswald was half this man's age and in all probability fitter than he, but the policeman fought like a demon.

One of the officers screamed at Oswald. 'Shoot the President, will you?' But the cry was all but lost in the confusion, as fists continued to fall amid Oswald's verbal protests.

Oswald struck the cop a good one between the eyes. That was the first and only blow he threw. Three other officers moving toward the scuffle grabbed Oswald from the front, rear and side.

'Okay—okay, we got him.' One said as another landed a punch squarely on Lee's left eye. The pain shot through his skull and dazed him, causing him to drop his guard for an instant. Before he could recover, all four of the cops were punching him about the head and body. Long ago at school, one of Lee's classmates had told him that when someone was beating up on you, the pain lessened as your body became more and more numb.

It was quite true. Lee could only see sparks before his eyes and feel a puffiness rising from his face.

'Look out, he's got a gun!' Someone shouted. A woman screamed and Oswald felt his .38 being pulled from his trousers.

'Okay, okay I got it.'

'I protest this police brutality,' screamed Oswald, all the fight knocked out of him. 'I am not resisting arrest, you're all witnesses. If they shoot me, you're all witnesses.'

Another officer put his hand over Lee's mouth but still Oswald tried to shout. Throwing his head left and right loosened the cops' grip.

'I am not–' His mouth was covered again.

There were now five officers carrying Oswald from the row of chairs. His head bowed, Lee knew he had taken a terrible beating. As his schoolmate had also reassured him, he'd know all about it in the morning.

Oswald and his captors reached the aisle. Lee was being held upright by the officers and he thought he heard the rattle of handcuffs. Two policemen held his wrists forward. Tilting his head to the left, Lee saw a policeman with a shotgun go in back of him. Suddenly, just as he thought he could feel no more pain in his body, another blow, which felt like a baseball bat, crashed into his back. He screamed, collapsing to the floor. As he was pulled to his feet again, Lee fought back tears of pain and frustration and shouted one last time. 'I have not resisted arrest!' His voice weakened, but he continued. 'You all saw this... you all saw this! You're all witnesses!'

Oswald's cries were lost beneath the shouts of the policemen as they hollered for everyone to get out of the way. One of the uniforms finally got his handcuffs onto Lee, securing his hands behind his back. Lee, by now supported by two officers, finally reached the foyer doorway.

Half staggering, half dragging his legs behind him and weak from the blows, Lee dropped in and out of unconsciousness, his head hung low, panting.

The shoestore man stood there, a look of sadness on his face. As Oswald lifted his head, their eyes met for an instant, but Lee did not recognize him. The shoestore man studied Oswald's face before he was finally dragged away to a waiting patrol vehicle.

A face dressed in abject terror.

Part Two
Interrogation

1

Lee Oswald, surrounded by five police officers, stared ahead at the elevator doors. The ascent to the upper floors was rocky, to say the least. The elevator was overcrowded yet silent. In any case Oswald was in a world of his own, collecting his thoughts for the interrogation to come.

Lee had already accepted the imminent battle where the personnel surrounding him would attempt to psyche him out, forcing him to incriminate himself. Lee knew the next few days would represent the hardest task so far in his entire life. A depression hung over him and an uneasy feeling filled his soul. Lee's stomach was tight as he desperately tried to formulate a plan to ensure his safe release.

Firmly gripped at the upper arm by a detective on his left side and by a police officer to his right and hand-cuffed behind his back into the bargain, Lee was trapped. Indeed, the elevator could only just hold the six people in it, they were all jammed together like sardines in a can - he couldn't fight or even resist, even if he'd wanted to.

The only consoloation was that if he was unable to swing a fist, they couldn't do so either. That thought in itself gave

Lee some minute comfort. Of course, he knew that once they were out of the elevator and in an office or interview room, that scenario would change immediately. Yet he continued to steel himself for the trouble ahead. Lee could smell his own perspiration and felt somewhat uncomfortable but he rightly figured that was the least of his worries. The policemen around him didn't seem bothered by it or at least weren't using it against him.

The gradual elevation in such a confined space was eerie. In the police car ride downtown, the officers had obviously been trying to intimidate Oswald, throwing punches and verbal abuse at him for any or every reason for the duration of the ten minute trip.

Although unpleasant, this had not perturbed Lee. As far as he was concerned it was all par for the course. He tempered his anger at the assaults by realizing that if any of the group saw him later, they'd see all too well what a rough time the Dallas Police had given him, thereby proving himself to be one of them. One thing had shaken him somewhat, something that had stayed in his mind since being dragged out of the theater earlier yet something he couldn't put his finger on. Now it became crystal clear. He remembered being pulled through the doors of the theater to be greeted by television cameras... rather strange, he concluded, that there should be a battery of cameramen who just happened to be outside the theater when all the commotion was reaching it's height. Then, when the police car screamed into downtown, down the Main Street ramp into the police vehicle area of the Dallas Police Department, there was another TV crew in position, filming him being brought through the basement.

Suddenly, Lee was thrust out of his thoughts by the jarring of the elevator as it came to an abrupt halt. Oswald glanced up and to his left and saw the elevator signal for the third floor.

'Okay,' said the officer at Lee's left, as the uniform at his right let go of his arm and wrenched back the elevator grill, then the door. 'Let's go, let's go'.

Oswald was swiftly pulled along by the policemen into the lobby. His shirt was hanging off his left shoulder, the singlet he wore beneath it exposed. The officers in charge of him walked Lee quickly, his hair still messed up and greasy from the fight in Oak Cliff. His back aching, his face swollen. As he walked through the lobby, Lee caught a glance of Bill Lovelady, one of his work colleagues at the Book Depository. Lovelady was sat, staring at him.

... what the hell is he doing here ...

Directly ahead of him by some fifty feet, Lee noticed the stairwell leading to the upper and lower floors. A patrolman was standing in front of the well going down to freedom. As Oswald and his captors left the elevator, Lee caught a glimpse of this officer unfolding his arms, placing his right hand on his revolver. Lee took slow, deliberate steps, trying to slow the entourage and set an easier pace but was forced along into the lobby.

'Come on, out of the way!' said a policeman behind Lee. Lee looked sharply to his right as a blur headed toward him. The swift movement startled him, then, as he tightened in fear, a flash erupted and momentarily blinded him. Confused but not injured, Oswald realized someone had taken his photograph. Reporters leapt toward him and Lee again saw evidence of television cameras in the hallway.

'I said get out of the way!' The officer screamed at the pressman. 'There'll be time for that later. Out of the way!'

He pulled at Oswald.

'You want a blanket for your head?' A calm, soothing voice said into Oswald's ear.

'No,' Lee replied. 'Of course not! I haven't done anything!'

Oswald lifted his hands and shook them. The handcuffs

rattled and again he slowed down so that the reporters behind and to the side of the photographer could see them clearly.

'Sergeant, what's he a suspect in? Why is he here?' cried a newsman.

The sergeant replied, 'Later boys. You'll get a story later. Right now, we gotta see the chief.'

The six men, followed by the newsmen, turned left into a narrow corridor, barely eight feet across. A tall man stood at the corner of the lobby holding a TV arc lamp as far above his head as he could. Oswald was still rattling his handcuffs and repeatedly tried to turn and say something to the reporters. As he did so, the officers in charge of him pulled him forward.

After two abortive attempts to turn and face the eager media, one of Oswald's captors spoke to him, quietly. 'You'll talk later. Remember your rights. Use them.'

Oswald was quiet. The policeman had a point and he acquiesced.

'You boys will be informed of any developments later,' said the sergeant to the newsmen, 'now, get off our backs'.

At his signal, two uniforms moved behind them and stopped the news people in the corridor. The newspaper reporters and photographers voiced their individual protests at the same time, Lee could hear them shout that this was their story, that they were here before their colleagues and that if anything came of this incident they ought to have access to the prisoner first. In the middle of this the two uniforms uttered various comments about them never again being allowed into the building, never mind this floor, if they weren't quiet, calmed down and moved back.

Oswald couldn't help wondering if they had any idea of the story that was about to break. Lee allowed self-importance to wash over him, afforded himself a sly grin. It took barely a second to erase that smirk as the enormity of the day smashed down any delusions of grandeur he may have been harboring.

Oswald was pushed to his right and he saw a wooden door with a glass front. On the glass, in chipped black lettering, were the words:

HOMICIDE & ROBBERY BUREAU

The small group moved swiftly into the office, the detective allowed Lee through the door first, just barely keeping a hold on him as he did so. As Oswald entered he saw a woman to his right sat a desk, typing. She looked up at him, slightly bewildered.

'Straight ahead, that door to the right,' said the detective. Ahead of Oswald was a large filing cabinet. Similar, he thought, to the kind you see in a library, solid wood, lots of little drawers, lots of little file numbers on the drawers.

He went directly into the office.

... this is it. This is the beginning ...but when, and how, would it end?

'Okay, now. Why don't we start right at the beginning?'

Oswald was sat at a tiny desk in the Homicide office. Around him stood several detectives, some talking among themselves and another on the telephone, just feet to Oswald's left. Lee could see into what seemed to be another office to his front right. The office door bore some name, but as the door was open, he couldn't make out the name inscribed on it. It wasn't so important, he reminded himself. The less he knew or remembered about this place, the better he'd sleep later.

The detective sat in front of him began again, calmly. 'I'll repeat myself, because I know you're confused and I know that you wanna get this straight the first time, just like I do.'

The policeman paused and Oswald's gaze fell on him, their eyes locking.

'Fine. Now let's get down to business. Don't let any of the other officers worry you or pressure you. You just take no notice whatsoever of them, they'll just be going about their business. Okay, first of all I'd like to get some background on you for this little piece of paper here.' The detective held up the paper. Oswald looked at it.

'Now, my name is Rose. Detective Gus Rose. Here's my identification'. Rose held up a gleaming Dallas Sheriff's Office badge encased in a leather wallet bearing his name and photograph.

'Okay. You now know who I am. I'm going to ask you to empty your pockets and show me your identification.'

Lee spoke quietly. 'Detective, in case you've not noticed, I can't help you in that because my hands are cuffed behind my back.'

As Oswald spoke, he tried to stand and show Rose his dilemma, As he did so, he was pushed back down into the chair. The action jarred his back and Lee grimaced.

Rose was sympathetic. 'Easy there, Carl. This man is doing his best. Take the cuffs offa him.'

The detective pulled Oswald up from his chair, jarring Lee's back again. This time, Lee was ready and concealed his pain. A key was produced and the cuffs taken off. Lee began rubbing his wrists as he sat down.

'That okay now?' Rose enquired.

... you sarcastic bastard ...

'Okay. Now here's what we're gonna do.' Rose produced a pack of cigarettes and a lighter. After setting them on the table between himself and Oswald, Rose looked Lee straight in the eyes.

'I'm going to ask you to stand and hold your hands above your head. Then Carl here is going to frisk you and empty your pockets. Okay?' Rose motioned to Oswald to rise. Lee did so, putting his hands high above his head.

'I understand that my friends who brought you in didn't have time to search you before they brought you in, so we're gonna do it now. Whatcha got there Carl?' The young detective already had his left hand in Oswald's left pocket, as he stood behind him. He pulled out various papers and other items. The cop held them in his hands and looked through them.

'Library card.'

Carl threw it over to Rose as he plunged his right hand into Lee's right hand pants pocket. Oswald stared at the card on the table in front on him.

'Well, now,' said Rose, looking at the crumpled blue card, 'who we got here then, Mmm? Ferrie. F–E–R–R–I–E. Doctor David William Ferrie.'

Rose looked up at Oswald, 'Then, that's your name?'

Rose sank back into his chair, taking a cigarette from the pack and the lighter from the table.

'No,' interrupted Carl, 'I don't believe it is. Does he really look like a doctor to you? I'd say not.'

Lee looked down at the table and cursed, silently.

Carl continued to rummage through Oswald's clothing, pulling an item from Lee's back pocket.

'Will you take a look at this!' The detective unclipped then tossed Oswald's brown leather billfold at his senior. As it hit the desk, it's contents spilled out over the surface.

'Okay, what do have we here?' Detective Rose emptied the remainder of the wallet's contents and spread them across the table.

He spoke as he counted some dollar bills onto the table.

'I make that … thirteen dollars and change. Check that would you, Carl?' Rose pushed the money over to his colleague and continued to go through Oswald's possesions, picking up and flicking through Oswald's note-book.

'This looks mighty interesting. Names, addresses. All kinds of things in here . . .' Detective Rose stopped at one particular page and studied it. 'New Orleans…' The detective again picked up the Library card and read the address on it. 'New Orleans…' he muttered under his breath.

'This card is from the Library in downtown New Orleans. Is that where you're from?'

Lee said nothing. Rose had all the time in the world and both men knew it.

'Okay, let's move on.' Rose flicked through the notebook quickly and then placed it to one side. The toe of the detective's foot was now visible over the desk as he rocked himself on the wooden chair. He whistled, low.

'Well, lookee here.'

Dropping his foot and using his weight to propel the chair forward, he and it landed upright with a heavy bang. Two United States Marines Selective Service cards appeared under Lee's nose as Rose leant forward. Both had a photograph of Oswald and both had the same biographical data, but only one bore his correct name:

Lee Harvey Oswald. The other was in the name of his sometime alias: *Alek J Hidell.*

'Which one of these fine servicemen are you, hmm?' said Rose, obviously intrigued at this little charade. 'You sure as hell can't be both and Doctor David William Ferrie. So, which one is it?'

Oswald fidgeted, then stated, 'I have not been read my rights. I do not have legal representation. I've done nothing wrong. You do not have the right to detain me here any longer.' Lee was panicking and, as he realized, shut up. Remaining seated, Oswald raised his eyes to meet Rose's, who by now was inhaling from one of his cigarettes. The senior detective remained very calm. A cloud of smoke erupted from his pursed lips.

'Which one are you?' he said, in a cold whisper.

Oswald snapped and leant forward, almost into Rose's face, the detective didn't bat an eye-lid.

'You're the cop,' Oswald said flatly. 'You figure it out.'

The tension in the room had suddenly increased and

Oswald was expecting more blows. Gus Rose remained calm. He had no reason to hit Oswald. He was in command of the situation and Oswald was not going anywhere without his say so. Then, the door to the corridor opened. In it stood a heavy, chubby man, standing all of five and a half feet, about fifty years old he was dressed in a smart dark blue suit. Lee Oswald turned to his right and looked at him. The man wore a large, white, Texan style cowboy hat, as did all the detectives. He didn't look at Lee, but addressed the officer behind Oswald.

'Carl,' he said quietly.

'Yes, sir?'

'Go organize a search warrant and take some men to...' he paused and looked at a scrap of paper in his hand, then continued, '...this address on Fifth Street in Irving and pick up a man named, uh–' he read again from the paper, 'pick up a suspect by the name of Lee Oswald.'

The man moved next to Carl and showed him the paper in his hands. Carl took it and studied it. As Carl moved toward one of the telephones, Rose interjected as he stood up.

'Why is he wanted, Captain Fritz?' said Rose, as Oswald looked away.

Fritz looked at Rose and spoke. 'Well, he was employed down at the Book Depository and he had not been present for a roll call of the employees.' Captain Fritz dropped his hand to his side waiting for some response from his officers.

Rose's face gleamed. 'Captain, I believe we can save you a trip.' He pointed at the now forlorn figure sat at the table, head bowed, teeth clenched behind tight lips.

'There he sits.'

2

Oswald was ushered into what he presumed to be the chubby man's domain, which lay adjacent to the Homicide Office he had been questioned those brief moments before. Handcuffed again, though this time, thankfully, to the front, Lee sat in the corner of the room, alone. The room was about twelve feet by eight, with light colored walls. Oswald assumed they had been light green at one time but obviously needed some repair to them. A desk, three chairs and several filing cabinets were the apparent occupants of the small neat office, though in the corner stood a wooden hat stand, adorned with a white, ten-gallon cowboy hat. To his left, Lee could see his captors through the glass partition of the upper wall, sometimes they had their backs to him and occasionally one of them would look around at him, observing him. Obviously, they were deep in discussion regarding him but he could not hear their conversation through the glass. The door was shut. He wondered if it might be locked.

Oswald new that Bishop would almost certainly be getting in contact with the Chief pretty soon and that he'd be out of this mess not too long after that. Thoughts of his cover being exposed were not yet uppermost in his mind, though he was concerned about the actions of the hit team and their whereabouts.

... how do I explain to them how I was picked up by the cops and then released ...

That, Lee summised, could only be sorted out later, when he was out of jail, his freedom restored. Oswald's gaze fell to the floor. The wooden surface was partly covered with a cheap, plaid carpet on which, for the most part, sat the desk. Looking up again, Oswald saw various documents and notes taped to the glass partition ahead of him, behind the desk.

If the rest of the office was neat and tidy, then the desk betrayed a certain amount of flurried activity. Two black telephones, a plastic pencil holder, buff folders, a ruler, erasers and a small pencil sharpener combined with various papers and photographs of mug shots littered the desk.

Activity continued to increase outside the office. Telephones rang endlessly, mostly unanswered, detectives and uniforms pushed and shoved each other through the Homicide office off to his right front and into what looked like an interview room. One individual, obviously an offender of some kind, was brought noisily into the Homicide office, pushed past the chubby detective and his colleagues and generally manhandled into the interview room. A big, burly uniform came through and followed the arresting officers into the same room. Oswald wondered if there might be any more space left to fill in there, considering the size of the guy. A half-smile touched Lee's face as he wondered what the man had said when the big cop appeared at the door.

Then he began to think of Marina and the girls.

...how would they react to all this? The President possibly shot, all the turmoil. And what of Ruth...

Ruth and Oswald didn't get on well at the best of times and this would surely drive the wedge even deeper between them now.

...but what do I care? We'll be out of her house for good soon, so what the hell could she complain about then ...she'll probably find something...

Oswald felt a little bitterness seeping into his soul and drank it, as he reflected that the only reason Ruth didn't like him was that Ruth herself was going through a divorce at that moment and that her husband didn't even talk to her, wasn't even living there at the house. Lee sat back in his chair and waited for the words to begin. Reaching up, Lee began to lightly press his face. It felt puffy and he wondered how he looked. His eye had calmed down somewhat and the throbbing was not bothering him so much. Straightening his back though was a different story. His spine ached where he had been hit during the scuffle in the theater and Lee felt he needed someone to take a look at it. Lee was brought back from the depths of his thoughts as he heard the chubby man's soft, Texan drawl invade his ears.

'Mister Oswald, I trust these officers have explained to you the reasons for your arrest and have complied with the laws of Dallas County and read to you your legal rights. Would you please confirm that they have so?'

The chubby detective sat opposite Lee in the office next to the homicide bureau. Present with this man and Oswald were Detectives Guy Rose and Carl Weatherfield.

'And who are you?' said Oswald, rattling his manacles.

The chubby man opened his jacket. Lee watched him and saw the officer's .38 revolver encased in its holster beneath his left armpit. Reaching into his jacket pocket, the detective pulled out a black leather wallet and held it up to Oswald's face. Lee could see the Dallas Police Department badge clipped to one half of the wallet and biographical data and photograph on the other.

'I'm Captain Will Fritz of the Dallas Police Sheriff 's Office. Now would you answer my question, please?'

'Why am I here?' Oswald said, angrily. 'No-one has told me what I'm supposed to have done yet. I'm being held against my wishes. I have–.'

Fritz cut him short. 'Mister Oswald ...'

Fritz leant forward and looked Lee straight in the eye. The detective's eyes seemed larger than normal behind his eye-glasses.

... this guy must be blind without those ...

Captain Fritz raised his voice. 'We can do this quietly or we can do this not so quietly. I would prefer that we talk to each other real nice, then maybe we can all go home ...but I must advise you that whichever way we do it, depending on what you tell us and depending on what conclusion we come to, if we do indeed reach a conclusion, that one thing is certain. I, definitely, will be going home tonight. What do you want to do?'

Oswald, at once fully realizing his dilemma and the truth in Fritz's words, conceded.

'Okay. Let's get on with it.'

'Fine by me.' The captain shrugged, got up from his chair and tapped on the window. Oswald followed his line of sight and recognized one of the officers who had ridden with him following his arrest. The officer turned and looked in the direction of Fritz, who in turn motioned to him to join them in his office.

As the detective came through the office door, Fritz began to speak.

'Mister Oswald, this is Police Detective Bob Carroll, who is one of the detectives who works for me. If you recall, he is one of the men who brought you down here to headquarters.'

Oswald eyed the officer with contempt. 'I recognize him.'

'Okay, now I'd–.'

As Fritz began to speak one of the phones rang. All five men looked at it. Its second shallow ring was interrupted as Fritz picked up the receiver. He spoke sharply.

'Fritz.'

A faint recognition spread over Fritz's face as a low buzz could be heard from the earpiece. Lifting his head and looking at the officers in turn, Fritz's gaze ended on his prisoner sat like a trapped mouse in the corner of the office. Fritz's eyes burned into Oswald, but he remained unshaken. Whoever was on the phone had a good deal of information for the Police Captain, this fact being betrayed by Fritz's short answers, spread over long pauses. Then he spoke at length.

'Yes, Gordon. That would be in order. I'll get onto it right away... no, there's no problem with that at all. Just a moment.' Fritz put the phone piece to his chest and said, 'Carl... would you go get me agent Bookhout? I believe you'll find him in the Chief 's Office.'

Detective Weatherfield left the office and then the Homicide area. Fritz returned to his telephone call.

'Yes, Gordon, he's on his way. He'll be with you shortly. Let me put you on hold... speak to you later.'

Fritz placed the telephone receiver on the table and pressed one of the buttons on the phone. A white light flashed on and off. Fritz stood and walked to the edge of the desk nearest Oswald and leant against it. Lee facetiously thought it would only be a second before the table collapsed under Fritz's weight.

'That was the FBI, Mister Oswald. They seem mighty interested in you.'

...this is it... Bishop must have gotten in touch with someone... I'll be out of this God forsaken place soon...

'Now', said Fritz, 'we're gonna have a real nice talk, just you and me and some of my officers. Then we can get this cleared up and, like I said, we're all out of here.'

Fritz returned to his chair and picked up some papers and appeared to be reading through them. Lee thought Fritz was stalling, but said nothing. Carroll hadn't taken his eyes off Oswald since he'd been summoned into the Captain's office. Lee could feel his eyes drilling into him, deep into his mind. Oswald looked over at him and momentarily held Carroll's gaze. Bob Carroll's expression didn't change, but Lee could see something in those brown eyes he didn't care for.

As this mental shakedown was in progress, Weatherfield arrived with FBI Special Agent Bookhout. Bookhout came into the office in haste, Weatherfield somewhat behind him. Lee watched the men as they returned. Weatherfield closed the door slowly and silently behind him. Before he did so,

Lee noticed the difference in atmosphere in the office and back out into the Homicide Office. For a tantalizing second, Oswald heard a police officer mention the President... then Weatherfield closed the door on the scrap of information outside the four walls of Fritz's office.

Special Agent James Bookhout was a tall, dark haired man of about thirty-five and wore the customary dark blue suit. Although he was hatless at this point, Oswald knew he would be the kind of person to wear one of those fedoras that FBI men favoured in Dallas. Somehow, Lee couldn't see Bookhout in one of those Stetsons the Dallas Police wore. Lee's eyes smiled secretly as he let the thoughts drip onto him.

...anybody who could even belong to this century and still wear one of those Goddamn cowboy hats like this crowd did, just about deserved all the abuse they got...

There they all were, full of themselves, running around like a bunch of crazy, lost kids.

...don't have a clue. Not a damn clue...

As his mind dropped back to reality, Lee caught sight of the ring on Bookhout's finger. It was gold, very impressive, considered Oswald as he tipped his head to get a better view of it. Lee wondered how the hell a Special Agent could afford something like that.

Lee noted Bookhout's shirt collar protruding from inside his jacket sleeve. It looked clean and crisp, though this didn't surprise him in the slightest. If Hoover's boys were anything, they were smartly dressed. Maybe not all that smart in the head, but neat all the same.

Agent Bookhout reached the desk as Fritz disappeared behind his papers. Totally ignoring the FBI man, Fritz screwed up his bloated features and settled into his chair. By all accounts, the papers must have been the most riveting information on the surface of the planet, such was Fritz's concentration.

Bookhout looked a little puzzled at Fritz's apparent hostility toward him, a strange reaction from the Captain to say the least. Oswald put it down to internal rivalry. He likened it to service in the military, if you can do the best job you can and trip your peers up at the same time, well, why not go for it?

...people don't change much. Wherever they're from or wherever they live... they're all pretty much the same....

All this aside, Bookhout seemed to be in control of himself and whatever his reaction to Fritz's mood, he didn't seem too upset by it.

...working in here must be the pits. As if the work wasn't bad enough, a guy also had to put up with this kind of shit at the end of it. Still it couldn't be worse than the mess I'm staring in the face right now...

Activity outside the office intensified as more and more different officers spilled into the Homicide Office.

Some came to the window partition and gazed in. Once they'd seen Lee, they seemed satisfied and moved away, passing papers, swapping notes and taking telephone calls. The Homicide Office appeared to be in chaos and Lee wondered how long the situation could prevail before Captain Fritz heard the growing disturbance and stepped out to do something about it. Fritz motioned to the phone. Bookhout picked up the telephone receiver and held it to his ear.

'Agent Bookhout.' A pause, then, 'Hello?'

Bookhout looked puzzled. Fritz, from behind his wad of papers, reached over and pressed the button on the telephone. The light stopped winking. Agent Bookhout looked more than a little embarrassed. He repeated his name.

'Agent Bookhout.'

This time, he was through. The earpiece buzzed with the chatter from the other end of the line. Bookhout listened intently, staring at the wall ahead of him. He didn't look at anyone, least of all Lee Oswald, sat to Bookhout's right.

'Yes sir, I'll do that immediately... yes sir.'

The line clicked and Bookhout replaced the receiver. He looked down at Fritz still engrossed in his papers.

'Captain', Bookhout began, 'Mister Shanklin would like Special Agent Hosty to attend this man's interview. Agent Hosty is known to this man.'

At the mention of this name, Lee looked sharply up at Fritz and Bookhout.

Fritz exhaled and threw down his papers. A bored look crossed his face and he suddenly looked tired.

'Very well,' he said. 'Get him. Let's get on with it.'

Oswald looked at Carroll. Bob Carroll just stared back as he leant against the glass partition, arms folded. Carroll turned away, looking over in the Captain's direction.

Captain Fritz left his chair and his office. Detective Weatherfield stayed with Oswald while the others, Rose and Carroll, followed Fritz back into the Homicide Office area.

Lee looked at Weatherfield. This detective couldn't be older than Oswald. Blonde, tall, handsome and cleanshaven, Weatherfield looked to Lee as though he should have been on a movie set rather than in a Sheriff 's office in downtown Dallas. Weatherfield glanced up at Lee then looked away, moistening his lips. Weatherfield was somewhat shifty, thought Oswald, uncomfortable. Lee wondered why and could only surmise that Weatherfield was in a new post, probably his first at that.

...sap...

As he thought this, Weatherfield suddenly got to his feet. Oswald's eyes widened and he straightened up in his chair.

...Jesus! This guy's a mind reader...

Oswald was a little startled.

Weatherfield's chair screeched on the wooden floor. He looked at Oswald as he stood, turned and then left the room.

The office door rattled on its hinges as Weatherfield slammed it. All the policemen and detectives outside the room where Oswald sat looked up from their work and discussions to follow Weatherfield through the Homicide office and out the door.

Lee allowed a wave of contempt to fall over him .

...what the hell was all that about...

Oswald slowly massaged his tired and battered face. In the few moments since all the police had left, Lee was still unable to get a hold on his thoughts.

...what kind of condition was the President in?

He'd have to ask someone soon.

Captain Fritz and the other detectives returned to the office. Fritz had even more papers in his fist now. As he sat down, he began to organize them into a neat pile on his desk.

The detectives stood around the little office, towering over Lee. They were all taller than he was to start with and as he was now seated, they loomed even larger. Fritz cleared his throat, the officers all looked at him as he did so.

'Okay, now,' Fritz shuffled the papers another time and tapped the remaining few renegade sheets in to place, exhaling loudly onto them. Frowning, having achieved his goal, he dropped them onto his desk where the papers skidded haphazardly across it, making a mockery of the previous few seconds.

'Okay, Mister Oswald,' Fritz looked up at Lee and met his gaze from behind his eyeglasses. 'Just a few things I'd like to get out of the way before we get into why you're here.'

The Captain reached out for one of the many pencils in the plastic pencil holder sat squarely on his desk. After selecting the sharpest of the bunch, he then produced a piece of blank paper from his desk drawer. He began to write.

'Okay. Your full name, please.'

Lee sat up in his chair. 'Oswald. Lee Harvey Oswald.'

'So. This, uh...' Fritz picked up one of the cards found in Oswald's wallet, '...this Selective Service Card, this Marine I.D. card, uh, with your picture on it, with the name Alek J. Hidell... is not you? You are Lee Oswald, is that right?' Captain Fritz scribbled onto the paper as Lee answered.

'Yes, sir. My name is Lee Oswald. I don't know anything about a Hidell.'

'Well, I have here in my hands two sets of identification. Both have your picture on them and one says Lee Oswald and one says Alex Hidell. Now, to look at you and see your face and you told me your name is Lee Oswald, then this throws doubt into my mind about just about everything. Who is Hidell?'

Oswald watched as Fritz threw down both identification cards onto the desk.

'Well, I told you. My name is Lee Oswald. I have an I.D. bracelet on my left wrist.'

Fritz motioned to Rose. The detective stepped to Oswald and pulled him to his feet.

Fritz saw the bracelet.

'Get that off him, Rose. Let me take a look.'

Lee looked down as Detective Rose wrestled with the bracelet.

'It would be a lot easier if you took off these cuffs and let me take it off,' protested Oswald at the manhandling.

'It would be a lot...'

Rose had the bracelet off. Putting one hand on to Lee's shoulder, the detective pushed the prisoner back down into the chair. Rose took a step to his left and dropped the bracelet into Fritz's outstretched hand. The Captain examined it, turned it the correct way up and read aloud.

'"Lee"', Fritz put the bracelet down on the desk in front of him.

'Do I get that back?' Lee inquired.

'Yes, you'll get it back, don't worry about it. Sentimental value, huh?'

Oswald nodded. 'Yes. My wife bought it for me,' Lee looked down at the floor.

Marina, where is she now?

'And what is your age, Lee?' Fritz looked up at his prisoner, interrupting Oswald's meditation.

'Uh, I'm twenty-four. My birthday is October eighteenth and the year is nineteen thirtynine. I'm twenty-four.'

Fritz wrote that down. Lee couldn't understand why Fritz didn't get one of his men to do it, why they weren't all taking notes.

'So,' continued Fritz, 'you were twenty-four last month?'

'That's correct, sir.' Lee shot a glance at Rose, covering the door.

'Well Happy Birthday for last month, Lee,' Fritz said, deadpan.

Oswald's eyes flicked from detective to detective. They all wore the same sad, removed expression. They seemed to train these guys to abandon individual expression and settle on a countenance of steel, that nothing would ever penetrate nor infiltrate. So cheerless and dejected, they were etched with the look of defeat.

Fritz continued talking and taking notes. 'Now, Lee. I understand that you work at the Texas Bookstore on Elm and Houston, near Dealy Plaza?'

'That is correct.'

'And how long have you been employed at the Texas Book store?'

'I started work there on October sixteen of this year.' Oswald shifted his weight on the chair. Rose eyed him, watching Lee's every move.

'Just before your birthday, right?' Fritz scribbled away on his paper.

'That's right,' Lee confirmed.

'And, uh, how did you get this job, Lee?' Captain Fritz at last looked up from his paper and desk and sat back into his chair.

...you look a darn sight more comfortable than I do...

'Well, the lady who my wife lives with, Ruth Paine, uh, she lives out in Irving. Well, a friend of hers heard that I was looking for work and she suggested to Mrs. Paine that I call the BookStore and offer my services. I, uh, did not call the BookStore. Mrs. Paine rang for me and fixed up an interview for me with Mister Truly, the Superintendent.'

'And you went along and secured the position.'

'I, yes, I went along the next day, and secured the position.'

Fritz paused, reading his papers. Picking up the eraser to his right, he continued to ask questions.

'Okay, let's back up a ways here,' the Captain began to erase some of his writings. 'Uh, your wife... she ... you don't live together?'

Oswald bristled. 'Mrs. Paine is a nice person. We aren't separated as such, my wife and I, we just can't afford a home right now.' Lee dropped his head, half in shame as he said these words. He remembered all to well the arguments with Marina about getting a place of their own.

'I live in Dallas and my wife, Marina, lives with our two children at the Paine's house, out in Irving.'

'Okay, Lee. When do you see your wife?'

'I ride out with a pal of mine who works at the Book Depository. He lives just a half block from the Paine's house. He takes me home weekends and I ride back with him Monday mornings. It's not my idea of a neat arrangement, but it's the best I can pull off at the moment.'

'Sure, I understand.' Fritz actually sounded sympathetic. He continued. 'What is that address? Mrs. Paine's?'

'My wife and Mrs. Paine live at twenty-five-fifteen West fifth Street, Irving, Texas.'

'Okay. Where do you work in the BookStore? What

exactly do you do there?'

'I fill out orders. Then maybe help the guys load the trucks that come in. It depends on what I'm doing and where I'm doing it. I'm all over the place.'

'Which floor would this be on?'

'The loading? That would–'

Fritz cut in. 'No, no. The order filling. Where do you normally work, what floor?'

'Well, mainly the first floor. But my work could take me to any of the floors. Today, I was on different floors. It depends on the workload and the orders.'

Fritz looked up at Lee. He put down the eraser and his hands flat on the desk. Looking Lee squarely in the eye again, Fritz spoke in a low voice. 'Mister Oswald, where were you when the President was shot?'

That was it. Lee was stunned.

The President had been hit.

Lee felt a rising spasm of grief, disbelief and fear climbing the length of his spine, on its journey to jolt his already confused brain. The words were simple, but their connotation was devastating.

'Then ... he was shot?' said Lee slowly, eyes a little wider. He leant forward, urging Fritz to tell him more, to tell him that the President was only wounded, only grazed.

Fritz looked the same as he had the entire interview.

'Yes, he was shot. In fact, Lee, he died about, oh, just over an hour ago.'

Calm, unruffled, unflappable.

Lee's mouth dropped open. 'He died?'

'He died.'

Oswald stammered into his reply, aching to ask more, desperate to tell these men who he was, what he was.

'Uh, I was on, uh the second floor. I was... let me back up.'

Lee muddled on, eyes darting from here to there, not registering anything, his mind in utter turmoil.

'The President's car turned onto Elm and started down to the overpass.' Lee brought his manacled hands up to his face. With his right hand, he pulled on his chin, feeling the whiskers crackle beneath his fingertips. 'I was on the steps with some of the guys. I saw the President go past and then came back inside the BookStore to eat my lunch.'

'What d'you have for lunch?' The question threw him for a second. Lee wondered if it was designed to do just that.

Lee shook his head and shrugged his shoulders. 'Ah, a cheese sandwich and, uh, a coke. One of the colored boys was there in the lunchroom. He saw me, said hello, then left.'

'What was his name?' Fritz suddenly became more interested, leant forward in his chair. Rose, Carroll and Weatherfield were also looking on with growing interest.

Lee shrugged again. 'Don't know his name, but everybody calls him Junior or something. I don't know his name. I went into the lunchroom just as he was leaving.'

'Now, Lee, I want you to think real careful now. What happened when you were in the lunch room?' Fritz was angling at something, but Lee couldn't be certain...

'Well, I finished eating my sandwich, then I went over to the coke machine in there and bought a coke. I had just gotten the top off and was about to take a drink when in rushes this cop and says "Come here", or something like that...'

Fritz turned his palms upward in surrender, as not understanding why there should be a pause at this point in the conversation.

'And?' Fritz said dryly.

'And I did. Mister Truly was with him at the time. This cop looked real mean, shoved his gun in my belly and asked what my name was. I told him and he asked Mister Truly was that right and Truly said yes it was.' Lee pursed his lips, then wetted them. The prisoner had them hanging on his every word.

'Then what happened?'

'They both ran out the door, back into the stairwell.'

There, such an anti-climax.

'Did you see where they went?'

'No, I couldn't see where they were after that, but I did hear them running upstairs.'

'Why did they run upstairs?'

Oswald shrugged.

...stupid question...

'Beats me'

Fritz came back, looking a little embarrassed.

'Where is the lunch room located?'

'At the north side of the building. At the rear.'

'Would that be at the main door, the doors into the Plaza?' questioned Fritz.

'Well, none of the doors lead directly into the Plaza, but I guess you mean the main entrance. No, those doors are at the south side of the building. I was stood in those doors atop the steps when the President went by. Then I–'

Captain Fritz interrupted Oswald again. 'Did you hear any shots, or anything unusual whilst you were on the steps?'

'No. Nothing unusual. People cheering, clapping. That kind of thing. After he went by, I turned back into the store and walked to the lunchroom.'

'How did you get to the lunchroom? Which direction?' Fritz began writing again. When he stopped, that paper full, Fritz reached into the desk drawer again for a fresh piece. Oswald stopped and watched him. Fritz looked up from his drawer.

'Go ahead...'

'Let me think. When you enter the main doors on the south side of the building and take a right, you go up those stairs two flights, then you have to walk right over the other side of the floor to the lunch room. It's at the other side of the building, the North side.'

'Did you pass anyone, see anyone?'

'No.'

'No-one at all?'

'No. I guess they were all outside watching the President.'

'Why did you leave after seeing the President, only seeing a short glimpse of him?'

Lee's response was cool, 'Well, how much do you need to see of a guy?'

Fritz frowned, then said, 'Had you seen the President before today?'

Lee tipped his head slightly to one side as if he could not understand the question. 'Do you mean in the flesh?'

Fritz nodded.

'No. No I hadn't.'

'What did you do after the policeman and Mister Truly left you?'

'Well, I left the building because there was so much excitement. I didn't figure there'd be any work from then on...'

Fritz held up one hand in a bid to stop Lee speaking. The Police Captain turned to the other officers in the room.

'You fellas want to say anything? Just don't get us in a muddle here, we're all doing our best.'

Agent Bookhout was the first to speak. 'Mister Oswald. Let me identify myself.'

Bookhout reached into his jacket pocket. Lee saw the .38 tucked neatly into its holster underneath Bookhout's armpit.

...these guys are walking arsenals...

Showing his gleaming FBI badge to Oswald, Agent Bookhout continued. 'There you have it. Now, Mister Oswald,' Bookhout flipped the wallet back over the badge and replaced it. 'Why did you leave the area? How did you know about all the excitement outside the building if you were inside at the time?'

Bookhout folded his arms and leant back against the door of the homicide office.

Lee scratched his head. 'After the cop stopped me, I guessed something was wrong. It's not everyday the President passes by and two minutes later a cop pulls his weapon on you. It didn't take much to figure it out. So I walked back along the same route I'd taken to the lunch room and went down and out of the front steps.'

'You looked surprised when we told you that the President had died. With all the commotion outside the building when you stepped out, didn't you figure that out also?' Rose spoke in his slow Texan drawl. Lee turned and looked at him.

'Well, you know, I didn't talk to anyone... wait up. I did talk to one guy. As I left, this guy ran up to me and asked if I knew where a phone was.'

'What did you tell him?' Fritz interrupted.

'I pointed through the Depository doors and he ran up the steps into the building.'

Weatherfield spoke for the first time. The others looked somewhat surprised by this.

'So you didn't actually speak to him, then?'

'Uh, I don't remember. I do remember pointing through the doors and him running through them. One thing struck me about this guy though... I really got the impression that he was a Secret Service agent or something.'

Lee looked away from Weatherfield, back in Fritz's direction. Fritz was sat even further back into his chair and was toying with a pencil.

The captain continued, 'What gave you that impression? Why should you think that, that this man–'

'Because that's how he came over. He just looked the part,' Oswald held his hands in surrender. 'Maybe I'm wrong.'

Lee clenched his teeth behind his lips. His eyes began darting to and fro at the policemen, watching them intently.

A rap on the door disturbed the sudden silence. Bookhout moved away as the door opened. In stepped a tall, dark man of about thirty-five. Glasses, dark suit and crisp, white shirt were in evidence as the man entered.

Fritz spoke, 'Agent Hosty, thank you for joining us. We've started already, so I'm afraid you'll have to bear with us and join in the questioning when you feel up to it.'

'I know who this man is, Captain Fritz. We have already met several times in the past.' James Hosty looked over at Lee, sat in the corner of the office and nodded. 'Mister Oswald.'

Oswald glared back. Fritz noted the intense feeling his prisoner obviously harbored for the FBI agent.

'Mister Oswald, please continue. You say you showed a man to a phone...'

'No, I didn't show him to the phone, I pointed to the phone. Anyway, I could see people running round every place, some women crying, stuff like that. Most people were running in the direction of the little garden up on top of the hill. So, anyway I figured something had happened and I remember thinking that there probably wouldn't be any more work that day, so I decided to go home.'

Lee could feel the growing tension in the room, especially now that Hosty had appeared. His mind began to drift around and around. Ruby, the fat pimp who'd patronized Oswald so many times in Dallas and in New Orleans that summer. Ferrie who was now implicated whether he knew it or not because he had carelessly loaned Oswald his library card and not gotten it back.

Lee grinned inwardly.

...Ferrie is such a smartassed idiot... the oldest trick in the book ...

Borrowing a library card for insurance, compromising another individual, whether or not they were knowingly involved. Ferrie, to be sure, was up to his neck in the whole business and he knew it.

…a strange guy, Ferrie…

Oswald eyed his captors again.

He remembered Ferrie from years ago, before the Marines, when he'd joined Ferrie's Civil Air Patrol. Ferrie had gone to great lengths to show his eager recruits how to fire a rifle using a telescopic sight. He'd even told them that he was working for the intelligence community.

..did we believe him? Sure, why not. Why should he lie to us…

Oswald's mind returned to more recent times. The summer just past.

…New Orleans …Camp Street …Ruby …Four thousand dollars still stuck in the bus station somewhere in New Orleans…

'So you decided to go home. Back to your wife, back to Irving?' Bookhout said, plainly annoyed at the sudden intrusion of his colleague Hosty.

'No,' said Lee, snapping out of his daydream. 'No. I went to my rooming house on Beckley.'

'And what did you do there?' Hosty spoke for the first time, Lee shot him a hateful glance and turned to Fritz whilst pointing accusingly at Hosty.

'That man accosted my wife. Does he have to be in here?' Lee's voice rose in anger, 'I'm under no obligation to answer any of your questions. I have not been advised of my rights, I don't know why you've brought me here! I have not been allowed legal rep–.'

'Mister Oswald,' interjected Captain Fritz, 'please try to remain calm. Now, that's a very serious allegation you've got there–'

'You better believe it.'

'–and we can look into it if you wish. As of now, there are more questions I'd like to ask you and I'm afraid Mister Hosty stays.' Fritz took a deep breath. 'Now. Let's carry on with the interview.'

'He doesn't need to be here,' Lee protested further.

'But he is here and he stays here,' confirmed Fritz, his voice rising for the first time, 'so let's get on with it.'

'Do you, Mister Oswald, or have you at any time, owned a rifle?'

...a rifle...

Lee was stunned.

...a rifle? What the hell kind of question is that ...

Lee calmed himself before answering.

'No, I do not own a rifle. But, ah, Mister Truly and some of the boys at the Book Depository were looking at one earlier this week. Tuesday, I guess.'

'Mister Truly, the manager?' quizzed Bookhout, suddenly interested.

Oswald directed his answer at him. 'Yes.'

'Could you tell us more about that?' Bookhout followed up.

Lee shrugged his shoulders and tightly closed his eyes for a second. It was getting warmer in the small office and he wouldn't have been surprised if even more officers came into it. Again he smelt the perspiration drifting from his shirt and tired limbs.

'He was just there with some of the guys, is all.'

'Well, was it Truly's weapon or–.'

'I don't know. I didn't talk with them or anything, I was just walking past and they were there, about five in all, looking at this rifle. I didn't think of it. I've seen enough rifles in the service to last me a life time.' Oswald paused, 'I guess I'm just not interested.'

Carl Weatherfield spoke again, this time with a little more confidence.

'Mister Oswald, what type of weapon was it?

Lee looked up to the ceiling closing his blackening eye. After thinking for a short while, he said, 'Couldn't say to be sure. Ah, had a 'scope on it. It was a high powered weapon ... my guess is that it was either some kind of hunting rifle or maybe a Mauser. I couldn't say. Like I told you, I'm not that interested in rifles.'

Captain Fritz interjected, 'Now, what is your address on Beckley? You told us that you–'

'Ten-twenty-six, North Beckley.'

'That's the Oak Cliff area of Dallas?' asked Rose.

'Yes. I went home by bus.'

'Tell us about that. The journey home.'

3

Lee Oswald left the Book Depository and walked east on Elm, towards downtown. Something was wrong and that was an understatement. Feeling somewhat panicky, Lee decided the best course was to follow Ruby's escape plan and head for Red Bird airstrip. Looking back at the Bookstore, Lee could see maybe sixty or seventy people milling around on Elm Street, in the Plaza itself and the grassy incline leading to the railroad yards. The crowd was blocking traffic whatever it might be, bus or private cars, even Police cars.

...could be a problem...

The bus on his normal route back home to his rooming house would take him back up to and down Elm, right into this confusion near the overpass. He kept walking. People were looking past him toward the Book Depository and he passed the Dal-Tex building, one block east of the BookStore.

Several more police vehicles shot past toward the scene; sirens wailing, some on the wrong side of the street.

Amid the chaos Lee kept to the inner side of the sidewalk, keeping as much room as possible between him and the road. At this point, he remembered his jacket, left hanging on one of the hangers in the first floor lunchroom.

... damn ...too late to go back ...

The building would be sealed off by now. How could he be so stupid? Still, he doubted he'd see the Book Depository building again, much less his jacket.

...still, should have brought it with me ...

Lee increased his step. His mind drifted to the thought of the snipers.

Had they hit their target? Was the arrogant Billy the hot shot that he had claimed to be in Mexico?

Lee was convinced that the snipers were as good as they had claimed. He had nothing to disprove the fact even if he had wanted to. They were all so sure of themselves.

Ferrie had pointed out that he had personally trained two of them, so they must have been good. But then Ferrie would have said that anyway and Ruby would have taken it all in... fat, gullible bastard that he was. Of them all, Ruby was the one Oswald despised the most.

Ruby always had a line, something nauseous to throw you, something he knew you needed and that he could get for you. Ruby, a proud man. A man for all seasons, as Ferrie had put it.

You need anything while you're here in Dallas? Jack Ruby is your man. Be it liquor, a woman or a weapon, just go down to the Carousel, show the man your cash and the world is your oyster.

Ruby had once bragged to Oswald that he'd actually known Al Capone back in his Chicago youth. Lee had neither believed nor disbelieved him. Ruby, he sussed, was a screwball, a little man ever gunning for a big time reputation he would never achieve in a month of Sundays. But those Cubans were something else. Boy, were they scary.

Lee had been on edge all the time they were around. It had taken all of his control to stop himself shaking when those guys were about. Oswald had decided they were all crazies about three minutes after he'd met them. Always smoking, drinking, fooling around, playing life to the full, one of them had said. Even the way they drove around was asking for trouble. The wrong side of the road, way over the speed limit. Whatever you could do wrong in a car, they'd do it and then do it again.

Billy was the odd one out from the group though. Lee had conversed with him the most, probably because he was the only American in the actual hit squad. Billy had been somewhat distant from the others, though he did take the girls and the booze as frequently and to the same excess as his colleagues, the sniper had a pleasant, disarming quality about him, as if he wouldn't hurt a fly. Sure, he was tough and could take care of himself, but he had this strange calmness about him. The other snipers hadn't spoken much at all, least of all to Lee and he preferred it that way. On no account did Lee want to get close to these men in a friendly way and he assumed they felt the same way. These men possessed an amazing talent, thought Lee, but sadly for them or their victims there was no other way that it could be channeled. They were, indeed, people of their times and they were going to do their level best to affect their times.

This thought lifted Oswald because he had set out to do his level best to ensure that they did not suceed. It would be a fight to the death but not knowing whose death would come first shook him to the core.

Reaching Lamar Street, Oswald came out of his abstraction. He'd walked almost seven blocks and missed his bus stop. Stopping on the corner and looking to his right, Lee could see the taxi stand, just outside the Greyhound Bus Station.

... Greyhound ...

Get a damn Greyhound to New York or someplace and he was away. Better still, catch the coach to Washington and go and see Mister Hoover himself. After all, didn't old John Edgar gratefully send me some money every month? Didn't Lee have on his person right now a Government check worth two hundred dollars? Mister Hoover would be happy to see him no doubt. After all, this agent had sent him the information that several people were just about to leave the country after taking a pot shot at Mister Hoover's boss, the President. And he had his Hidell ID on him. If he had to produce identification, no one would be the wiser.

Oswald saw his bus moving slowly toward him, gently plodding through the traffic congestion. He decided against the Greyhound - after all he had to get Marina and the kids to safety - Lee took yet another look around the area.

The bus had stopped a couple of blocks down Elm. Oswald walked to it, apparently unconcerned with all the commotion. People were now filing out of their places of work looking West down Elm, trying to catch a glimpse of... what? The President's limo had surely left the area now, whatever had happened. Strange. All these folks eager now to see some trouble, or maybe even blood, could have seen the President as he passed them.

...takes all types ...

Oswald rapped on the bus doors. The driver opened them, a loud hiss accompanying the motion of the double door, the hydraulics moaning as they pulled their metal weight for the ten thousandth time. Oswald dropped change into the pay box next to the driver and walked down the center aisle, arm over arm as if he were swimming toward an empty seat. The coolness of the bus enveloped him and he felt relieved. Looking around as he moved enroute to the seat, he noticed Mrs. Bledsoe, the woman who'd asked him to leave her rooming house so bluntly back in October.

...she owes me two bucks...

Had it been another day, if he could have maintained an argument with her, for he was in no doubt he'd get that if not the money, he'd have mentioned it to her. But now definitely wasn't the time.

Mrs. Bledsoe saw Lee and looked away. Lee grinned as he

passed her and sat down.

The bus was now at a standstill in the heavy traffic. Lee began to ponder his wisdom regarding this particular mode of transport. He had just over an hour to get to Red Bird. Ferrie had warned them all that the plane would not wait for anyone past two o'clock and Lee knew he meant business. He strained to look up Elm to see if a break in the traffic was likely. Judging from what he could see, it was not.

...damn...

Maybe a taxi could get him to his rooming house in time. He needed his revolver, he wasn't about to trust any of these bastards, whatever had or had not been achieved today. As he contemplated his next action, the bus driver opened the doors again. A motorist was out of his car in front of the bus talking to the driver.

...hell, even if the traffic were clear this damned idiot's stopped the bus anyway. What the hell were they talking about at a time like this ...

Oswald made his move. Like a demon he was up and at the driver's side in a second.

'Give me a transfer, please,' he said, interrupting the conversation hailing back and forth down the steps to the man on the pavement. The driver looked up at Lee and punched him a ticket. Lee turned and looked again at Mrs. Bledsoe one last time, just in time to see her look sharply away, ignoring his stare.

'There you go, buddy,' said the driver. Oswald quickly stepped off the bus, crossed the street and headed the couple of blocks south to the Greyhound station and the waiting taxis.

*

'So the bus became stuck in the traffic?' Detective Rose, still leaning against the glass partition of the office, spoke slowly and deliberately, his Texan drawl evident in his voice.

'So you decided to take a cab?'

'That's right. I'd be on that bus now if I hadn't gotten off.'

'Mister Oswald, how come you were–'

'I said to you, that I'm not prepared to answer this man's questions...' Hosty was cut dead by the captive protesting to Captain Fritz.

'He insulted my wife and practically accosted her. I won't answer any of this man's questions.'

Hosty looked pinched. He the pair glared at each other.

'And what do we achieve with that?' Hosty countered, 'You're under arrest and the Captain has already told you that I'm staying. You may as well answer all the questions. You're hardly going anywhere until you do.'

Fritz interrupted, obviously tired of this bickering, 'Mister Oswald. Let's get on with it.'

'I will not answer this man's questions. I told you that before and now I'm having to tell you again. I can't make it any clearer to you.'

Lee's chagrin was evident, Hosty shuffled on his feet, clearly uncomfortable with Oswald's outbursts. The prisoner was not showing him any respect and he was in danger of losing a good deal of credibility within the room.

Eventually he continued, 'Mister Oswald, have you been to Russia?'

All the detectives in the room shot glances at each other; Lee bit the bullet.

'Yes'

'And how long did you stay there?'

Now Hosty began taking notes. Fritz looked down at his desk and the paper on it as Oswald continued.

'I was there almost three years. I left the United States in October nineteen fifty-nine. I got back in June of last year.'

'That's June of sixty-two?' said Hosty.

'Yes, June of last year.'

Lee did not look at Hosty, his answers aimed in a quiet

voice to the desktop in front of him. Hosty, now at last getting something from the prisoner, moved quickly.

'Have you at any time written to the Soviet Embassy in Washington D.C.?'

'Yes, several times.'

'Did they reply?'

'Of course they replied. They always reply. Any Embassy would reply. It's what they're there for.' Lee glanced at the ceiling and down, and began to rattle his handcuffs.

'Have you ever been to Mexico? In particular Mexico City?'

...where the hell is this guy going...

After a pause, he replied. 'Yes, I was in Mexico City only this Fall.'

'And what was the reason for your visit to Mexico?'

Hosty was moving in on something, Lee was convinced.

...could Bishop have told Hosty about Mexico... unlikely - but what if Bishop can't get me out of the station? Could he have detailed Hosty to do it for him? Would Hosty do that – for me?

Lee could not afford to let his cover go– just yet.

'I don't think that's any of your damned business, Hosty. Count yourself lucky you've gotten this much out of me.'

Captain Fritz moved into the quagmire. 'Mister Oswald. Let's all remain calm here–'

'Calm? You want I should be calm?' Lee changed the subject. 'This man practically accosted my wife on two occasions. Why should I be calm? He didn't need to do it. He upset her, asking all kinds of things. Why should she put up with that? Listen, if you want a definition of calm, then that's me. You haven't told me why I'm here yet, I haven't got a lawyer with me and I don't have to answer any more of these questions.'

'We'll get to that, Mister Oswald,' said the Captain. 'Now–'

'I have difficulty understanding you. How can we 'get to that' when I don't know what the hell I'm here for! Tell me why I'm here.'

Captain Fritz retained order in the interrogation. His years of experience with prisoners a good deal more belligerent than Oswald held him in good stead.

'You want an attorney? You can have any attorney you want. If you can't reach one, the court will appoint one for you. Is that satisfactory?'

'Yes. I'd like to call an attorney in New York City. His name is John Abt.'

'Do you know him personally?' asked Fritz.

'No, sir, I don't.'

The Captain sighed and looked to his right at the detectives standing around his office.

'Okay, let's proceed. Carl, if you would, please.'

Weatherfield stepped forward to the Captain's desk. Reaching into his jacket pocket, the young detective pulled from it a .38 Smith and Wesson revolver, similar to Oswald's. He placed it on the desk and stepped away.

Captain Fritz pushed the revolver toward Lee with his pencil.

'Do you own a gun like this, Mister Oswald?' Fritz looked at Oswald. 'Pick it up... take a good look at it.'

Oswald grinned. 'Captain, you know I'm not going to pick up that gun. Nice try, but I'm not going to pick up that gun.'

Captain Fritz took Oswald's refusal in his stride. 'What did you do when you reached home?'

'I changed my trousers, they were my work trousers and they were dirty. I changed my T shirt, changed into a clean one, picked up my pistol and went to see a movie.'

'Why did you pick up your pistol? Why would you need that to go and see a movie?'

'No reason,' lied Oswald, 'I just carried it, you know how boys do when they have a pistol.' Lee shrugged his shoulders and looked away from Fritz's eyes.

Rose interjected 'So you weren't expecting any trouble or

such?'

Oswald looked at him. 'No, I just carried it.'

'From where did you get the gun?' said Weatherfield.

...here we go... here they come ...

'From Fort Worth. When I lived in Fort Worth in the spring. I don't recall the name of the shop where I bought it.'

'Did you buy it for a specific reason?' said Rose.

'No, I just bought it. I just wanted it.'

Captain Fritz re-entered the fray. 'Where did you go to school, Mister Oswald?'

'I went to school in New York and later in Fort Worth. Then I joined the Marines. After that I continued with my high school education in that service.'

Hosty moved behind the Captain, trying to put himself in Oswald's vision.

'Were you trained in weapons whilst in the service?'

'Sure, just like everybody else. I told you before, I've seen enough rifles to last me a lifetime.'

'Did you win any medals for rifle practice or shooting or whatever you might call it?'

'Yes, I won the usual medals.'

'How would that reflect your marksmanship with a rifle?'

'Uh, let me think about that one. I wasn't a good shot at all. I didn't win any of the various competitions and I can't think of anyone in the unit that would want me to be on their particular team. I wasn't the worst shot in the unit though. So, to answer your question, if I told a person who hadn't been in the service that I got medals that showed I was a sharpshooter, then they'd probably think I was a pretty damn good shot. But that's not the case. I don't recall exactly, but I got very low marks and only just made sharpshooter, which is minimum requirement.'

'So you would need to be on the range for however long it took to get that requirement.'

'Yes. Practice makes perfect and all of that. In my case, I'd say that practice made just about minimum score to pass for minimum classification. But I wasn't the worst shot.'

Fritz took a long, slow breath, put down his pencil and rubbed his face. Lee heard the sharp crack of the day's bristles on Fritz's chin. Fritz wetted then sucked his lower lip before he continued.

'Mister Oswald, Let's get some more background before we go in to specific areas...' the Captain looked over the top of his spectacles at his prisoner, 'that okay with you?'

'Sure.' Lee paused, then asked, 'How about some coffee or something. I'm pretty thirsty.'

'Okay, we'll go with that. But later. We'll move on. Now ...' Fritz shuffled his papers again as he collected his thoughts.

Gus Rose stood against the frame of the doorway, then moved away to remove his jacket, hung it in the corner on the hat stand and moved back to the door. Oswald could see Rose's revolver in his shoulder holster, it occasionally caught the light, Lee was momentarily mesmerized by the shining metal.

A weapon in such pristine condition was obviously in the hands of a professional.

It was all Lee could do not to allow a slight grin to appear on his swollen face as he recalled the many times he'd been chastised for not cleaning his rifle in the Marines, a task he had laughingly tried to bribe DelGado and Thornley to achieve for him while he caught up on his *Das Kapital* studies.

Agent Bookhout stood between the hat stand and Rose, seemingly lost in the confinement of the small room, even more than Lee was. If anyone was feeling the strain of this interview, it was Bookhout. Oswald was amused. An agent of Hoover's mighty FBI squirming in a tiny office somewhere in Texas. A depression hung menacingly over Bookhout, like a rain cloud about to burst.

Lee considered the condition of the President.

Then Billy had been as good as he had boasted. The sonofabitch. He'd gone and done it.

Lee took a long, deep breath and held it for several seconds.

Where does that leave me? Ferrie would have left by now, the others would probably have gotten away... maybe not... maybe they're in custody, too...

Oswald couldn't be sure of that.

...situation's getting out of hand... if Bishop or even Hosty don't get me out of here soon I'll need to blow my cover, tell them my FBI number. If Bishop doesn't appear, Hosty will have the means to check it out, to admonish me in the eyes of these police officers.

There are a hundred angles on how to deal with it. First, I'd need to ask Fritz to clear the room, get all the others out except maybe Hosty or Bookhout and tell Fritz that I'm willing to talk only to him or the FBI. Then would come the bombshell of the FBI number. It would only need a phone call to Washington to clear that up. But do I need to tell them just what the hell I've been up to? Shanklin, the FBI agent in charge of the Dallas Field, will intervene somewhere along the line. Fritz would have to tell Shanklin about the matter because Hosty or Bookhout would anyway...

Lee let go a breath. He was rambling to himself. Trying to consider every angle under the sun was not going to help his present position, he'd have to deal with this step by step, steer clear of any leading questions, such as those Hosty had tried to put in his path earlier.

Bob Carroll hadn't stopped staring at Lee for the entire interview. Lee caught his stare for a second as he glanced about the room. The detective's eyes were adhered to Oswald's. Lee felt their iciness drilling into his head. He dismissed it. If Carroll was there just to intimidate him that was fine. One less voice suited him down to the ground. Lee looked at Carroll, arms folded stood in the corner opposite him. A tall man, slim with dark brown hair.

...those eyes...

His shirt looked worn and frayed and his brown suit not too dissimilar. Lee found himself wondering what a Dallas detective's salary might be. He found himself willing to wager a year's pay against a Dallas Detective's that his was the lesser sum, he being paid only two dollars an hour. But that was cover. Cover that soon might need to be discarded for survival.

Captain Fritz spoke at last, 'Now, Lee. I'd like to go over your, uh, political beliefs... if you do indeed have any. You do, I take it, have some opinions?'

Lee leant forward onto the desk in front of him, manacled hands laid out in front of him. As he studied his shackles, he spoke in a quiet, confident voice.

'Captain, I don't have any political beliefs regarding the United States, or at least any that are concerned with the United States. I am the Dallas chapter President of the Fair Play for Cuba Committee. Their headquarters are based in New York City. The address is in my notebook.'

'I'm finding lots of things in your notebook, Lee,' Fritz shot back, 'it makes very interesting reading. Please continue.'

'Well, as I was saying, their headquarters are in New York City although I have never visited that particular building. I was also Secretary for the same organization during my stay in New Orleans this summer.'

'Am I to believe that you support the Castro revolution?'

'Yes, that is correct. I do support the Castro revolution. This whole Castro thing began while I was in the Marines.'

'What did your superiors in the marines think about this?'

'Nothing was said to me at the time. No one said a thing. Several of my fellow servicemen were finding out their Marxist beliefs at the same time that I was. My own unit sergeant was an advocate of the Castro revolution.'

'I find it hard to believe that the Marines would let any of their number preach this kind of stuff,' interjected Hosty.

...goody for you, Hosty...

Lee looked at the FBI man, 'Well, you'd better.'

'Let's not get heated again. Let's just get on with it, shall we?'

'Fine with me,' said Hosty, trying to gain the upperhand, but with whom it was not clear. Oswald looked away through the glass partition, wondering when the coffee would arrive.

'Are you a member of the Communist Party?'

'No. No, I'm not. And never have been. I will say I am a Marxist though.'

'What would be the difference between the two?'

'There's too much to go into here. I'll just say that there is a difference, but it's much too complicated to explain in one or two sentences.'

'Do you think we'd understand?'

'I'm sure you'd understand, but I not so sure that you'd agree with me.'

'Hmm, well Lee, we'll pass on that one for now. What are your feelings for the President?'

'Kennedy? Well, I guess... I admire him. My wife loves him. I didn't vote for him and probably wouldn't have, had I been here. I have nothing against him, let's put it that way.'

'Would you say that President Kennedy was against Castro?'

'Not necessarily. That Bay of Pigs thing. He stopped that, didn't he? I guess he's not against Castro, per se, but,' Lee shrugged his aching shoulders, 'I wouldn't say that the President was a Marxist, either.'

'Well, right now, he's not anything, is he?'

'Guess not.'

The door opened and a police officer came into the room. Squeezing past Gus Rose, he handed Captain Fritz a piece of paper. The Captain read it slowly, glanced at the other side of the paper and then, finding nothing there, turned it back over and read it again.

'Mister Oswald. Says here that you rented your room on North Beckley under the name of O. H. Lee... can you tell me about that?'

'Easy. The landlady obviously got confused with my name. Easily done.'

'Couldn't be that you didn't want anyone to know who or where you were, could it?'

'I can see why you might think that way, but no, it's perfectly innocent. Anyone could make a mistake like that.'

'And that's all you have to say on that, nothing more you want to add?'

'Nothing more to add. Say,' Oswald changed the subject quickly, trying to catch Fritz with his guard down, 'can I ring my lawyer now? I'm being held here against my will. You people haven't told me what the situation is about yet, about what I'm supposed to have done! It's ridiculous! I want a lawyer, Captain, it's the only way.'

Oswald sat back in his chair. It creaked as his back stopped on the backrest.

'Mister Oswald, as I told you earlier. You can have any lawyer you wish. If you don't know one, we will get you one. It's not a problem.'

'Well, Captain, it is a problem if only because he's not here yet. How can there be no problem when I don't even know why I'm here?'

'You probably think I'm stalling,' replied Fritz, 'but I can tell you that's not the case. On the whole, Mister Oswald, I think if anyone's stalling, it's you. Now, if that comes as a surprise to you, I'm sure you'll let us know your feelings on that. I think you know what the situation is and I hope that you'll come to your senses sooner rather than later and tell us what we want to know.'

Oswald sat, his face blank and his eyes looking directly into the Captain's.

...cat and mouse... just what I've trained for. Three years playing an extremely dangerous game in the Soviet Union was more than enough to see me through this charade. Fritz is bluffing. Of course, the Captain has some crumbs, a little suspicion, but that's the man's line of business if not his nature. I've played before with bigger stakes and won. This situation isn't any different from the Russian experience, a lot less frightening for sure, but... even though in Russia I was very much on my own, the Soviet President hadn't been attacked whilst he travelled through Moscow or Minsk. That, I can't dismiss.

Again, he decided, it was almost time to tell someone what he had been up to that summer and autumn, but then again he refrained.

...a little more time... a little more time...

'I know it's hard for you to let it go, Lee,' continued Fritz, 'but I suspect that you do have a great deal to tell us.' The Police Captain eyed his papers as he doodled on them. 'We're all here. We have got a lot of time. Why don't you tell us what we want to know?'

Fritz was casting a line and Oswald knew it.

...they know nothing, nothing... he's fishing... just giving me enough bait...

Agent Hosty spoke, filling the silence. 'Captain, I'd like to ask a few questions... routine, a little background, things of that nature.'

Fritz sat back in his chair, his legs splayed out under his desk. 'Go ahead,' he threw down his pencil, 'be my guest.'

James Hosty sat on the chair in front of him and to the right of the Captain. He pulled a silver fountain pen from his inner breast jacket pocket and a notepad from one of his outer pockets. As he wrote on a fresh page in the pad, he asked, 'Mister Oswald, I'd like to go over one or two points with you, purely routine, just for the record. Okay?'

Oswald took a deep breath and sighed, shrugging his shoulders.

'Okay, I'd like to get some more background on this, if you would just bear with me,' Hosty pulled off the top of his pen and pushed it onto the other end, crossed his legs and balanced the note pad on his knee. 'Now, uh, when you left the Book Depository, did you leave the area immediately?'

Lee sighed. His hands were now in front of him, resting on the desk. Lee pondered the metal shackles binding his wrists. His long fingers wrapped around themselves, intertwined as if in prayer. His mind again began to wander, to Irving, where Marina was, where his daughters were and to where Ruth was, the woman hell bent on wrecking his marriage just because her own was going down the tubes. Lee wondered what, if anything, Ruth was filling Marina's head with, all day long and most of the nights.

... just what might she be doing to our relationship?

True enough, Marina and Lee hadn't gotten along that well since they returned to the States eighteen months ago, they'd certainly had their ups and downs like any couple... but Lee knew and he knew Marina knew, that they were going through a bad spell right now, that was all. Their only major concern was to get some money to get a place of their own, so they could live together without people pestering them, telling them how to run their lives, interfering with them, all four of them. Just to be left alone, to sort themselves out.

Oswald remembered the summer before. After his work on the bogus Fair Play for Cuba Committee, Bishop had spoken of the new NASA facility down in Gentilly, Louisiana. Lee had already been ear-marked for a position in the photographic lab, probably something to do with the Space Program, Bishop mentioned the Apollo Moonshots due to begin in Sixty-Seven. Lee had attended a seminar in Moscow in May of Sixty-One and the first man to ride in space, Soviet Cosmonaut Yuri Gagarin, had been guest of honor. Lee had been excited to attend the seminar, the fact that Major

Gagarin had been there in person so soon after his historic flight had been the ultimate icing on the ultimate cake.

The NASA job would be well paid too, enough to buy a house and get well away from family and neighbors, well meaning or otherwise. Put this together with the four thousand dollars locked away in the post office in New Orleans and his FBI checks every month…

The thought of the Government voucher in his wallet flooded into his brain.

…damn… should have cashed it last week and wired it to New Orleans…

Oswald slowly closed his eyes as the realization hit him.

…soon, if not already, the entire Dallas Police Force will know who I am… my cover shattered in the Dallas area once and for all…

Of course, he was about to reveal himself to the FBI in Dallas sometime today but the thought of the police finding that voucher was something he hadn't contemplated.

…just what does Hosty know at this point… has he already been informed of the voucher… Hosty will know immediately what it is, even if it takes the police an hour or so to find out… what about Bookhout… does he know… and Fritz…

Lee was troubled by this. There were things in his billfold that he could explain away, albeit with a certain amount of tribulation on his part, but the voucher was something else. Even if he could persuade the authorities that it didn't belong to him, how was he to explain that he had the voucher on his person? They would conclude that he had stolen it, which would be the obvious solution and a viable one on their part. Lee was stuck with this dilemma.

…maybe a private word with Hosty or Bookhout is the solution… but would Fritz allow me that…

The Captain was about to let him talk to Lyndon Johnson before he'd let these G-men talk to him in private. Oswald calmed himself, breathing slowly and deeply to suppress his growing fear. There was absolutely nothing he could do, he decided to let them worry about it.

...don't answer any of their questions on it... it's their problem to explain it, not mine to justify it...

Lee opened his eyes to see Hosty and Fritz gaping at him intently. Lee came out of his stupor, trying to hide this internal revelation from his captors.

'Uh, after ...'

'What did you do after you left the building?' repeated Hosty, impatiently.

Lee glanced around before saying calmly, 'We covered that. I got the bus and went home.'

Fritz took a sharp peek at Hosty who wrote quickly onto his notepad. The enmity Fritz held for the FBI in general and this agent in particular was evident to Oswald. Lee grinned inwardly, marveling at the clandestine actions that undoubtedly befell the rival factions of government agencies. He wondered at the man-hours lost because of the petty politics, misinformation and so forth.

Hosty was rattled, to say the least. The FBI man was stumbling on almost every question and was obviously quite unprepared for this interrogation session. Oswald knew the assassination of the President had something to do with it, had he not found himself in this dilemma, he too would have probably been a little more distraught. In fact, Lee knew that his trauma was far greater than Hosty's could ever be. After all, whatever Hosty knew about the details of the actual shooting, he couldn't possibly know who'd done it.

'Mister Hosty,' said Fritz, 'I think-'

Captain Fritz was interrupted as a uniformed officer knocked and poked his head around the door of Fritz's office.

'Excuse me, sir, but a detective has something important to tell you outside.'

'Be right there, Peter,' replied Fritz to the officer. As he stood to go, Fritz said, 'Please carry on. I'll be just outside.

I'll be as quick as I can.'

Fritz left the officer who closed the door behind him before pointing to a young man approaching them in the Homicide Office. Oswald watched intently. The others in the room were talking at him, but he ignored them. As they tried to get in Lee's line of vision, he altered his stance, moving his head and eyes to see the activity outside the office.

The young detective was looking directly at Oswald, over Fritz's shoulder. Fritz nodded and then turned to look at Oswald also. Both men re-entered the Captain's office. The detective did not take his eyes from Lee's. Lee stared back.

The Captain began speaking, but Oswald missed the beginning of the conversation.

'... sure that's him?'

'That's the man I saw, yes sir.'

Oswald couldn't remember seeing this man before. Was it possible that he could be...

The Captain continued. 'Mister Oswald, this detective said he saw you run down the hill on the north side of Elm Street just after the President was shot, is that correct, detective?'

'That is correct, sir, but about ten to fifteen minutes after the last shot.'

Lee Oswald knew that whoever this man had seen, it couldn't have been him.

...I was already in the cab at about that time, on my way home ...

'You got anything to say on that, Mister Oswald?' Fritz drawled.

Oswald slowly rose from his chair and leant forward, the palms of his hands down on the old desk. Lee looked at the detective. His cover was being stripped away, slowly but surely. Lee was desperate. He had to get out of this place or talk to someone in private.

...where in Hell's name is Bishop...

Everybody looked at Oswald but no one tried to refrain him from standing. They were all shocked by his action.

Lee gritted his teeth.

Something has to give now, but he was no longer in control of the situation. Something had to be said and it was down to him to say it.

...okay, they can have it all, every last one of them in the room. I'll give it them, Chapter and Verse... are they ready for this... are they ready?

Lee breathed in deeply and swallowed it.

...no... this is not the time...

He would need to be in charge of whatever situation was going on around him and right now, he wasn't. Still, he couldn't resist one line, one line to bewilder his stunned opponents. He turned his gaze to the Captain and said, almost inaudibly.

'Everyone will know who I am now...' He sat down.

Fritz turned to the officer, saying, 'Outside.' Both men left the office again, ignoring Oswald's outburst.

Lee sat back into his chair and watched them leave. The Captain said something to the young detective, who then left the Homicide Office.

Bookhout had moved across the Captain's office and was standing with his FBI colleague, engaged in whispers. Weatherfield, Rose and Bob Carroll looked about them in bewilderment. Rose looked at Weatherfield and shrugged his shoulders, Weatherfield looked at Carroll with the same expression on his blond face.

It was obvious to Oswald that no one else in the room had any idea what all this was about.

He, of course, knew the greater plan, but couldn't think who the young detective could have seen running away from the scene that could have looked so like Lee for the officer to think it was him. Another one of those minor things that Lee was going to let the police worry about.

Fritz was now engaged in deep conversation with two different officers, still outside his office.

...Jesus... this guy spends more time out of this place than in it ...but there we go...

Fritz appeared at the door, a weary look in his eye. Oswald almost felt some amount of sympathy for the man, but held it at bay. As Fritz opened the door and returned, Lee noticed he was holding even more pieces of paper. Over the Captain's shoulder, back in the Homicide Office, orders were being shouted at everybody and anybody who came near the door. Several times uniformed officers appeared at the glass partition only to be waved away by Bookhout or Rose. Chaos seemed to be the order of the day and he was grateful for the apparent calm within the room. Lee didn't think that this peace could prevail for much longer.

'Bob, have we taken this man's prints?' said Fritz.

'No sir,' replied Carroll, 'nor have we taken his picture.'

Fritz remained near the open office door. Looking around the office, then down at the papers in his hand, he said, 'I think we can leave that a while. We can finish that later. Right now, we need this man in a line-up. We should move on that right now. Mister Hosty,' the Captain looked at the FBI man. 'Forgive me on this, but I'm sure you understand the situation. Time is against us. We'll get this guy's prints after the line-up and then we'll talk some more.'

Oswald looked at Hosty.

..line-up...

4

Two uniforms rattled on the bars of Lee's cell. He sat up on his bunk and looked at them. The shadows fell onto him, the sunlight shining through the windows ahead of him outside the cell.

'Time for some more, Oswald,' said the taller one, turning the lock. The two officers grinned at Lee and each other.

He ignored them, threw his legs over the edge of the bunk and stood up.

'Stay where you are until I say.'

The jail door creaked as the officer with the keys pushed it open.

The tall policeman waved Lee toward them, saying, 'Okay, Oswald. Move it, nice and easy.'

The officer's hand rested on his weapon, nestling snugly in its holster, leather creaking as the pressure of the officer's limb came upon it.

Lee moved past the officers, into the semi-dark corridor and waited.

One officer gripped Oswald's left upper arm and guided him to the jail elevator. They moved slowly toward the doors. They were already open, waiting to envelop them in their descent to the third floor and more questioning.

...what now... more line-ups... more futile questions, more insults ...more so called evidence?

'What gives?' said Lee, as the three men stepped into the grimy elevator. He turned around and forward, facing the door. One officer looked at him, saying nothing.

'Fingers,' said the other, slamming the elevator door.

The other officer threw the lever and they dropped from the fifth floor high security area to the third.

Lee felt his stomach growling, 'Lunch time yet?' he inquired, 'I'm starved...'

He glanced at the officer to his left, who simply stared ahead.

Lee inhaled deeply, held it, then let it go and looked down at the metal cuffs, tight and binding.

...what will the girls be thinking...

A tidal wave of emotion hit him, almost taking him unawares and Lee felt tears welling up in his eyes. Taking another deep breath, he controlled himself.

The elevator dropped and hit the third floor and stopped

with a sharp crash. Lee wondered how long it would be before the cable supporting the elevator snapped…

As he appeared in the corridor, the news reporters flooded around him yet again. Lee breathed in sharply, feeling his sore ribs as he did so and moved into the fray.

The reporters pushed and shoved their microphones into his face.

'Oswald, did you shoot the President?' said one, pushing in front of a police officer and standing in front of the prisoner.

Lee's reply was rapid and to the point.

'I didn't shoot anybody, no sir. I haven't been told what I'm here for…'

The police officer bringing up Oswald's rear pushed Lee into the Homicide Office doorway.

'Do you want a lawyer?' someone said, as another camera flashed.

Oswald stopped and resisted the officer's momentum.

'No, sir, I don't… I've just been…'

Detective Gus Rose appeared at the door, saying, 'Okay, do you want to go through?'

Lee and his captors filed through into the Homicide Office area. The prisoner and two uniforms passed by the Captain's office.

…another room to squeeze me in…

The trio carried on down through the Homicide Office. As they passed Fritz's office, Oswald glanced over to his right. Captain Fritz and the chief of Police, Jesse Curry were evidently deep in conversation with Forest Sorrels. None of them saw Lee and his guard as they passed.

The small office door to Lee's left was closed, a sign placed upon it with the legend:

DUTY OFFICER

Lee pondered on that information as he was led swiftly to *…where?*

...what the hell is a duty officer?

A sharp turn to the right and Oswald was in a grimy, run down office that he couldn't imagine anyone doing their best work in. There was no window in the room, although it was slightly larger than the Captain's office. As Lee and his guards entered, he could see the old chest in front of him, several name cards in metal holders bearing identification and the whereabouts of files. To the right an old bureau, the wood stained with what Lee took to be spilled ink. Atop the bureau stood an old angle poise lamp, straining over the desk area of the bureau. Several papers were splayed over the desktop, some hanging over the edge, randomly thrown down. Some others were on the floor.

...must be the first people to enter this place this century...

As they moved to the desk, the officer to Oswald's right pulled a piece of paper from a file on it and fastened it to the desk top. Lee looked at it. Clearly, he could see the separate areas for fingerprints.

RIGHT THUMB and RIGHT INDEX, it shouted.

'Take the cuffs off him, Manny.' The second policeman produced the key to Lee's bonds. A sharp click and he was free.

'Give me your right hand,' said the officer, sharply. Lee held up his right hand as ordered. The officer took a hold of Lee's right thumb.

'Relax,' he said, shaking Lee's hand at the wrist. The officer looked at Lee and the prisoner looked back. 'Just relax.'

Oswald watched as his thumb was rolled in the ink by the officer. He felt a certain spark of embarrassment, of humiliation as this procedure was thrust upon him. Then, in turn, all of Oswald's prints appeared, one by one, on the scrap of paper. When his little finger had been dealt with and while the policeman fixed a different, clean piece of paper to the desk, Lee beheld his ink covered fingers with disdain.

The operation was repeated with Lee's left hand and the

officer passed Oswald a cloth to wipe his hands. Lee took it and did so, but some of the black ink stayed on his finger ends and in his nails.

He threw the towel to one side and looked at his fingers again.

'That's it, finished,' said the officer in charge, 'let's go.'

Oswald was handcuffed again and as he turned, he saw Sorrels, Curry and Fritz peering at him through the glass partition of the Captain's office. Their faces long and grim, Lee expected the worst. He was pushed back into the Homicide Office area and then pulled left into the Captain's office.

Oswald sat in the same corner as he had for the previous day's interrogation.

He looked at all the faces in the room, faces he was becoming familiar with. Captain Fritz, Chief Curry, who got up and left as Lee entered, Sorrels who also left with the Chief.

...Nash... Grant... two others I don't know...

'Lee,' started Fritz, for once not looking at his notes but at Oswald, 'a development you should be aware of. The FBI have asked me to ask you if you would comply with them and take a polygraph test, that is, a lie detector test so we–'

'No,' said the prisoner, firmly. 'Definitely not. See my lawyer about it, when you people let me reach one. I have refused them before and I'm not about to change my mind now, no sir.'

Oswald sat back into the chair and looked away.

'Did you like President Kennedy, Lee?'

'What kind of a question is that?' Oswald retorted. 'Sure, I like President Kennedy and I do have my own views on national policies, but, as I told you before, I'm not answering those kind of questions, so forget it.'

As Lee again moved into the corridor outside the Homicide Office, the atmosphere was charged with both menace and bewilderment, both for Lee and the officers who escorted him. Normally, the trip to the elevator would have taken seconds, but this was not a normal day. Tens, if not hundreds of T.V., radio and newspaper reporters jammed into the narrow corridor.

Oswald and the policemen either side of him were swept along on the crest of a human wave, the center of the storm. From Captain Fritz's quiet office, where Lee had spent the previous two hours since his arrest, to the gauntlet he and the officers were now running, no-one could have anticipated the rush of feeling and emotion that swelled as soon as the first reporter yelled, 'It's him, here he comes!'

The roar increased as microphones and questions were pushed into Lee's fearful face. To hear anything above the deafening noise would have been impossible, to answer, a miracle.

Agent Bookhout, who had not initially entered the fray on Oswald's behalf, found himself pushed, pulled and generally manhandled as he tried in vain to get past the encroaching reporters. Lee saw Bookhout turn his head back in his direction, a look of controlled fear on his face. Bookhout began yelling for the reporters to get back, to let the prisoner through, all to no avail. Not one of them gave way as they tried to get to Oswald, to get any information out of him.

Lee felt even more trapped than before as the policemen in charge of him battled through the throng. Pulled like a rag doll through this mass of hysterical humanity, he began to feel his bruises and his back began to ache.

Shouts from the officers surrounded by the reporters went totally unheeded as the small group fought their way through.

Suddenly, Oswald's left arm was almost ripped from its socket as the officer to his left pulled him into a lobby area. The reporters tried to follow, but were first ordered then pushed out of the lobby. As the din subsided, a curious silence enveloped the small room. Ahead of them were some toilets and then immediately to their left was a single elevator door.

A police sergeant stood in the open elevator doorway.

'This way.' The sergeant said, holding back the door. The two uniforms either side of Oswald hurriedly walked with their prisoner into the elevator.

'Jeez,' said one, as they entered the elevator and turned, their backs to the wall and facing the open door. 'D'you ever see anything like that?'

No one replied as the sergeant stepped out of the crowded elevator and slammed the iron door shut. One of the policemen elbowed Oswald in the ribs, Lee instinctively brought his hands up to his face.

'Not gonna give us any trouble now, are you buddy?' he said, bellowing into Oswald's ear.

Oswald remained silent, his manacled hands touching his chin. One officer stabbed the elevator descend button and they were on their way.

'Basement coming up,' chuckled one.

The lift shaft was dark, only one tiny light revealing that the elevator was in use. Bumping and rattling, the lift shaft dropped down from the third floor.

Lee still couldn't understand what the line-up could be about. It couldn't be in connection with the President's shooting, they'd have spoken about that during the interrogation. Oswald desperately searched his mind for a clue as to why he should be forced to stand in a line-up.

Lee's mind again flew in different directions.

...what is Ruby doing now? Where is he?

The officers in charge of Oswald couldn't know who he really was and what he'd been up to during this stay in Dallas anymore than he knew what was going on around him. Something was going on around him, something serious and something over which he had no control over.

It just didn't make sense. All Bishop had to do was call the police or Hosty or Bookhout and they'd release him immediately. Despite the fact that Lee's cover was almost wrecked by now, what with the newsmen and all, he still couldn't grasp why all this talking was going on.

... Bishop... Bishop ...

The elevator hit the basement level soundlessly, only the shaking of the door revealed that its journey had been completed. The doors were pulled back.

Oswald stood in the doorway that led to the viewing room. Either side of him, as always, stood his two shadows, the unspeaking, faceless uniforms that he knew no more about than he knew what was going to happen during this press interview. The uniforms moved away to be replaced by two detectives.

The door to the viewing room was slightly open and Lee could see Chief Curry, Fritz and other policemen just through it, deep in discussion. He could hear the chaos in there. Newspaper reporters were hollering at each other and Lee guessed there must have been a hundred if not more people filling every available square foot of the area.

As the door opened further, Oswald saw the TV cameras in front of the newsmen and figured the ranting and raving was caused by the cameras blocking everybody's view.

Curry signaled to the men in charge of Oswald. A uniform stepped forward and opened the door for the three men. The detective to Lee's right pushed in front of him and went through the door first. Lee felt his arm brush against the detective's pistol, nestling below the policeman's armpit, beneath his jacket.

Lee was pushed through the doorway by the other detective. As he emerged into the viewing room, the atmosphere reached fever pitch. Shouts rang out and a mob situation was stirring. The detectives tightened their grip on their prisoner and stopped, looking for reassurance from their Chief as to whether they should proceed.

Curry motioned them forward and at last Oswald faced the crowd.

Questions were thrown at Lee as he stood before the reporters and T.V. crews. Standing bewildered amongst this assembly was as unnerving as it was frightening. Finally, as the reporters lost some of their desire to be the first answered, sanity prevailed.

Lee began to speak, portraying more confidence than he realized he had.

'I positively know nothing about this situation here. I would like to have legal representation.'

Several reporters suddenly called out, Lee lost their questions in the noise and answered as best as he could.

'Well, I was questioned by a judge…' Oswald shrugged and paused as he tried to remember the judge's name, but could not.

He continued as he glanced around at the multitude of faces gazing blankly at him. 'However, I protested at that time that I was not allowed legal representation during that very short and sweet hearing. Uh, I really don't know what the situation is about.

'Nobody has told me anything except that I am accused of, ah, of, uh, murdering a policeman. I know nothing more than that. I do request, uh, someone to come forward… to give me, uh, legal assistance.'

Beyond Oswald, chairs, tables and any object that could be used to climb onto were being scraped across the floor as the reporters tried to get closer and closer to Lee. As they did so, the detectives holding his upper arms tightened their grip on him.

'At ease!' someone yelled, interrupting Lee's flow for a millisecond.

Recovering instantly, Oswald tried to get closer to the reporters directly in front of him, ignoring those behind and to the sides. They were too far away and couldn't possibly hear him, the host of T.V. cameras stopped their colleagues getting anywhere near Oswald.

Wanting to tell them the reality of the situation, hoping one of them would ask a relevant question, Lee became increasingly desperate. The detectives slowly began to pull him back to the doorway of the viewing room, but he resisted.

'Did you kill the President?' asked one reporter in an amazingly, softly spoken voice that Lee heard despite the noise around him. The newsman was cool and calm and Lee could hear him perfectly.

'No ... I haven't been charged with that. In fact nobody has said that to me yet. First thing I heard about it was when the newspaper reporters in the hall, uh, asked me that question.'

Lee's voice was now trembling somewhat. He was scared. Indeed, no one had said that to him. Why should they?

'You have been charged,' said one reporter.

'Nobody said what?' said another.

Oswald wasn't sure what he'd just heard. The noise about the place was almost as bad as in the corridor outside Fritz's office, back on the third floor.

Leaning forward, Lee looked inquiringly at the reporter directly in front of him. 'Sir?' he said, looking directly into the man's eyes, almost pleading for him to repeat that question.

He said it again. 'You have been charged.'

Oswald looked to his left and up. This was where the question had come from, not in front. Lee looked at the other reporter - a curtain of disbelief rapidly falling over his agonized face.

'Great,' he muttered under his breath. He was stunned, for the millionth time that long day.

He didn't believe it, couldn't believe it, and wouldn't believe it. The cameras whirled and the light bulbs flashed.

For a second no-one spoke, Lee's eyes glazed over and all he wanted to do was get out of this place, to run and run. Of course, he could not. Sadness filled his empty soul.

The policeman to his left pulled Lee away from the reporters and the small group of men moved back to the doorway entrance to the viewing room. Lee drifted slowly away, head bowed.

...you have been charged, the reporter had said... you have been charged...

The words echoed in, through and around his head.

...charged with murdering the President... but no one has mentioned that. In all the hours I've spent in the police department today, no one has mentioned that.

'Mister Oswald, what were you doing in Russia?'

Lee looked down to the floor as the detectives pulled him away.

A newsman moved toward Lee as he progressed to the doorway and said, 'Mister Oswald... how did you hurt your eye?'

Lee stopped, pulling away from the now slack grip of his captors. Leaning forward, pushing his bruised face right up to one of the T.V. cameras, he said, 'A policeman hit me.'

The detectives pulled him away toward the door. Lee heard someone shout for the door to the elevator area to be opened. Lee left the reporters, the T.V. cameras and the esteem for those he had worked for back in the viewing room.

And more than a little of his soul.

Oswald was taken back to his cell on the fifth floor. Apart from a solitary policeman at the end of the corridor, he was alone.

He sat on the bunk in semi-darkness, a small light from the stairway to the left was on. Holding his weary head in his hands, Lee pondered his fate.

...tomorrow... tomorrow all this will end. I'll be free ... and then

watch me go…

He looked up and just caught a glimpse of the officer guarding him. The uniform's shiny cap badge glinting in the twilight, like a lighthouse beacon beckoning in the darkness.

…so …they've charged me …charged me with the President's death… but that's okay, this will all be cleared up tomorrow …and tomorrow I'll be gone from here…

Oswald felt limp. He was exhausted. In one eighteen hour spell, he'd put in half a day's work, been beaten up and charged with two murders, abused by the police, not allowed legal representation, paraded in front of the world's media, forced to stand in line-ups when he didn't know what for … interrogated, finger printed. There was little wonder he felt confused.

Lee lay down on the bunk and stared into the gloom. He wanted to scream, but knew that wouldn't do any good. Better he lay quietly and recharged his energies for the fun and games tomorrow.

Turning over onto his right side, he closed his eyes.

He wanted to sleep, but was afraid to. He needed to sleep, but knew if he managed any at all, it would be a restless sleep.

Oswald turned onto his back, slowly and stared at the ceiling again putting his hands behind his head.

5

Captain Fritz reappeared in the doorway. The movement of the glass in the door as he opened it was evident to everyone's eyes. Lee had visions of the glass falling out as he entered, smashing onto the floor like in some Laurel and Hardy movie or an episode of 'I Love Lucy'. Somehow, Lee decided, he couldn't see Fritz ousting Desi Arnaz as his wife's co-star.

The two men that Fritz had been talking to outside the office moved in closely behind the Captain. Both were quite tall and both had short, neat, dark brown hair. Lee guessed they were more FBI, judging by the expressions on Hosty's and Bookhout's faces.

They moved in, neither paying much attention to Oswald. The office was becoming overcrowded by now and Oswald wondered who'd be allowed to leave. He'd be happy to forget the false arrest, the fight, the beating.

...just show me the door and I'll walk...

The first man, Lee estimated, was about thirty-five to forty years old. He had one of those faces that looked thirty to forty when he'd been nine and would stay that way until he was eighty, which was pretty good when you were eighty. The man's nose was quite long and his ears protruded at an odd angle. Clean-shaven, but already with a shadow, the man had startling, piercing blue eyes. Lee had only seen one other person with eyes as piercing as his and she was the mother of his two children. A dark blue suit completed his professional appearance.

Captain Fritz returned to his chair opposite Oswald. He pulled it back and its legs scrapped on the bare wooden floor.

Fritz sat and looked down at his notes, putting some other papers he'd brought in with him into the right hand drawer of the desk. Fritz looked up at Oswald.

'Mister Oswald. These two gentlemen would like to ask you several questions. They will, of course, identify themselves to you should you so wish it.'

The man Oswald had observed as the trio came into the office pulled out the usual black leather wallet and flicked it open. Lee stared at the gold Secret Service shield hanging on the inside of the wallet.

'My name is Kelley, Thomas Kelley and as you can see I am with the Secret Service.' Kelley turned to his left and pointed to his colleague.

'This is Secret Service agent David Grant. Mister Oswald, we'd like to ask a few questions ...'

Kelley smiled as he moved toward Lee and stood in the corner that had been occupied by Weatherfield next to the hat stand. Kelley folded his arms and leant against the glass partition pulling a silver cigarette case from his inside jacket pocket as he did so. Oswald was quiet as Kelley rummaged his side pockets for his cigarette lighter.

'Now,' Kelley pulled his hands from his jacket pockets and thrust them deep into his trouser pockets, still searching for the elusive lighter.

'Here, let me,' Grant was there with his lighter already lit, holding it beneath Kelley's cigarette.

'Thanks, Dave,' said Kelley, as he took a long drag at the cigarette.

Oswald saw the red end glow and Kelley exhaled, blue smoke bursting from his lungs into the room.

'Okay now, Mister Oswald,' Kelley put one foot on the chair and leant both his arms onto his right thigh, 'I'd appreciate your full co-operation on any and all questions that we may ask you. We'll get through this a whole lot sooner if you just answer our questions sharp and to the point. I understand that you have been advised of your rights to counsel and that you are willing to speak to us...'

'That's bull,' interjected Oswald. 'I haven't been advised of my rights and I have not been allowed to contact an attorney to represent me. I object to this treatment. I have been wrongly charged with two crimes I did not commit. I have been paraded in front of the world's media as an assassin... how the hell am I going to walk the streets now?'

Kelley held up his hands, cigarette smoldering in one. 'Hold on, hold on. We have all day on this. We can take it one thing at a time. Now,' the Secret Service agent took a long, final drag of his cigarette, 'would you like to tell us about your views on the President?' Kelley stubbed the cigarette out and put the flattened stub into his jacket pocket. Lee watched him.

'I will tell you this,' said Lee, waving his finger at all of the officials stood about him in the office, 'I have lived in the Soviet Union and have been interrogated by professionals, do you understand me? You should be aware of that. I do not need to answer anything you ask me. I want my attorney. I'm saying no more.'

'You have had the opportunities to phone your attorney,' said Captain Fritz, showing more impatience than anger, 'and the person you wish to see is in New York. Fine. But, Mister Oswald, it would help both of us if you allowed us to furnish you with an attorney from here in Dallas. We could save a great deal of time and finally move ahead on this.'

Kelley nodded in agreement. 'You can call Mister Abt on the jail phone later. It's not our fault he didn't answer your call yesterday.'

Oswald conceded, 'I don't have the money for the call,' he said, defeated.

'Then call collect,' said Fritz. 'There are ways around everything, Lee.'

Kelley continued. 'Lee, I also understand that Mrs. Paine has been trying to reach New York for you also. If you are as innocent as you say, then you don't have too much to worry about, do you?'

Oswald looked away through the glass partition of the Captain's office. He felt tired, trapped and scared as he recalled last evening's revelation, the news reporter revealing to him for the first time that he had been charged with the murder of the President. The arraignment before the judge was but a dim memory, almost a dream, paling into insignificance at his first rendezvous with notoriety.

Activity outside the Captain's office was beginning to hot up again as the morning wore on. More and more uniforms were passing through, sneaking glimpses in Lee's direction, hoping for an eyeful, no doubt, of the President's assassin.

Oswald was past caring by now. His cover could go to hell, he was in serious trouble and he knew it. Neither Hosty nor Bookhout had said anything to him about his relationship with the FBI and he wondered if they'd spoken of it to any of the Dallas Police. He had to doubt it.

Lee had to face it. He wasn't an agent of the FBI, just an informant. Hosty and Bookhout need not be aware of that and as for any payments he might receive… well, probably only Bishop could verify that.

…but what of Bishop… where the hell could he be?

He obviously hadn't been in touch with anyone at police headquarters; had he done so, Lee would have been out of police custody by now.

…so what the hell is going down here? Arrested and charged with murdering a police officer one minute, told by a reporter that I've been charged with murdering the President of the United States the next… no legal representation… Hosty and Bookhout not knowing the ins and outs of my case, and no Bishop… no Bishop …

The enormity of the situation was trying to break down the mental barrier in his head. That the barrier was crumbling, there could be no doubt. But he had to deal with it. Lee subconsciously realised that there was going to no easy way out. He suppressed it, giving himself a headache doing so. His left eye was now half closed from the fight the day before but his body's pain had eased somewhat. He'd been surprised that he'd suffered no more abuse during his detention and believed that the police hadn't quite known how to deal with him.

Trying to console himself, Lee pretended that his arrest and the charges laid before him were Bishop's way of protecting him. By now, Bishop would be talking with the police, proving Lee's case to them. The police, as always, were dragging their heels on this matter and slowing down the moment of his release, proving to themselves they were masters of their own territory, not letting even a Presidential assassination on their patch ruffle them.

Lee again began to think of Marina.

...she must be going through hell ...

And his mother too, though she'd been through hell every single day of her life, as she was fond of telling everybody. It was easy for Lee to dismiss Robert and Edward. Lee had never really known his elder brothers, though it had been decent of Robert and his wife to let he and Marina stay with them in Fort Worth after his return from the Soviet Union.

Lee squirmed for a moment when he remembered that he still owed Robert one hundred and thirty dollars. To think he had four thousand in cash in a post office box in New Orleans. Still, he'd fix it later.

'In fact, Mrs. Paine has been making calls to your mother and brother for you. And to your wife.'

Lee said, shaken, 'What do you mean, to my wife? She...'

'Mrs. Oswald has been moved away from the Paine's house. And the children. The Secret Service have her holed up in a hotel outside of Dallas,' Fritz delivered this bombshell with his usual mild tone.

'On her own?' Lee raised his voice, his anger covering the tremble in his speech, 'She can't speak English, do you know that? What are you doing to her?' Lee rose from his chair, feeling his frustration and letting it show for the first time.

'You bastards! What has she done? She...'

Kelley stood upright, taller than Oswald. Grant too moved toward him. Kelley stopped Grant and motioned silently for him to back away.

'Lee, Lee,' said Kelley, softly. 'Marina and the girls are okay. The Secret Service has an agent fluent in Russian with her at all times. They are all fine and being well looked after. Believe me, in view of yesterday's events, it's for the best.'

'But I haven't done anything wrong. Why should they be in any danger?'

'I really don't believe that you're that naive, Lee. Whether you're innocent or not, some nutcase out there isn't going to worry about that.'

Kelley was right.

'And your mother has been to see Marina today. I understand she's with her now...' Kelley looked over at Captain Fritz, who nodded.

...mother ...my mother getting something right, not thinking of herself for a change... another day of hell for her... she'll love it...

'Let's get back to it now, Lee,' said Fritz.

Oswald looked at him and calmed himself. Lee clenched his teeth behind tightly closed lips. The thought of Marina and the girls alone with strangers whether they spoke her language or not was not one he could swallow easily. He looked down again at his bonds and wished they'd take the damned things off. Lee rubbed his face and said nothing.

'You said yesterday that you took a bus home, after leaving work. A taxi driver has come forward this morning and says he gave you a lift in his taxi at around twelve thirty yesterday. We found the bus transfer when you were searched. Did you take a cab?' Fritz looked up from his notes. Oswald's eye was distracted for a moment as more people came into the Homicide Bureau.

'Yes, uh, yeah.'

Oswald averted his gaze back to the Captain, who was busy finding a pen in his jacket pocket. Lee wondered if the Captain had been home the previous night, Fritz's eyes were red rimmed and he looked somewhat fatigued.

'Yes. The bus got caught in the traffic. I got the cab at the Greyhound station on Lamar.'

'Okay,' said Fritz, striking a line on his paper, 'that clears that up. Anything else you want to add on that?'

'Yes. When I was about to get into the cab a lady came up

who also wanted a cab. I said she could have the one I was getting in, but the driver told her to get the one behind.'

'So you took the bus and then completed your journey in the cab?'

'Yes.'

'And the fare was?'

'Uh, eighty five cents.'

'Eighty-five cents ... okay. Now, we ... a guy who says he gives you a lift to work from Irving, when you stay at the Paine's house.'

'Yes. Wes. He gives me a lift home on Friday nights and back into Dallas on Monday mornings. He lives just down from the Paines.'

'But this time you went home on Thursday night?'

'That's right.'

'Why?'

'I went home to get curtain rods for my room on Beckley. There are no curtains, no curtain rods. Ruth Paine had some in her garage. I figured I'd use those.'

'Did you ask her if you could have them?'

Oswald paused.

... *no* ...

'Don't remember,' he said.

'Couldn't the curtain rods have waited another day?' said Grant.

Oswald looked at him and answered. 'Sure. They could've waited another week.' He shrugged.

The Captain's phone rang. The conversation stopped mid flow. Fritz answered.

'Fritz...'

The Captain nodded as a metallic voice came down the wire into his ear. 'I'll be right with you.'

Fritz stood, slowly. 'I have to leave you gentlemen for a while. The photographic people have come up with something. I'll be right back.'

Fritz tapped his papers into a semblance of order and neatness and put them in his tray. No one spoke as he donned his Stetson and left the room. As he opened the door, Lee could hear the phones ringing in the Homicide Bureau and the chatter of many voices, some restrained, some loud. The door closed behind Captain Fritz as he turned to his left and disappeared from sight.

Oswald sat back into his chair and tried to relax. A wave of depression lapped slowly over him and his eyes again looked down upon his shackles. He tugged at them, pulled them sharply away from each other, testing their strength. His wrists were sore, having worn these damn things for the best part of twelve hours. Thankfully, the handcuffs had been removed during the night, though he hadn't slept well at all. Considering the circumstances, he wasn't surprised by that.

Lee's sleep, disturbed and fitful at best, hadn't been helped by his awakening at around one-thirty a.m., shortly after the newsmen had told him that he'd been charged with shooting the President. Two detectives had taken Lee down from his fifth floor cell to Captain Fritz's office. He was then put before the same Judge as earlier and advised that he was being held in connection with the assassination of President John Fitzgerald Kennedy. At that point, Lee wondered why on earth the world had been informed about his alleged crime but not him.

Lee's mind drifted once more to the others in the hit teams.

...what are they doing now... have they been apprehended yet ...

Maybe Bishop was keeping quiet so the others would not know that Lee was an informant in general and informing on them in particular. But, if he didn't know of their whereabouts why should they suspect his? The whole thing was odd, to say the least.

He needed to speak to Hosty or, preferably, Bookhout about his role in the scheme of things. Hosty, Lee didn't care for and he was sure the FBI man's feelings for him were about the same. If Oswald could get to Hosty and tell him who he was and prove it, that would just about blow Mister Hosty's head off.

... no ...Bookhout's the guy ... but how do I get to him ...

Two more men entered the office.

Steel eyes met theirs. Kelley looked over at Oswald. Lee stared back, feeling no good signs in the atmosphere.

'The Captain said we'd find the prisoner here,' the taller man spoke, a mop of gray hair disguised his true age but Lee guessed he wasn't yet out of his thirties. He had a chiseled, craggy, yet somehow handsome face with a sharp nose and gleaming teeth. Throw in a strong even tan and the habitual suit and there he stood. Lee glanced at the suit, neat and blue. A white shirt finished with gold cuff links. His necktie was not quite red, more of a pastel shade than true red. The man looked very smart, thought Lee, a little too smart for this time of day. At last, he produced his identification and showed it to Kelley.

Lee looked at the man's accomplice. Although he was smaller, he was still taller than Lee's five-nine.

Everybody is taller than me ...

It didn't worry him to much. He knew he was only average in height, but what the hell. The other man was dark, though not tanned. His jet-black hair shone in the electric light and he had heavy eyebrows and beneath them deep brown eyes.

They look like Feds ...

'I take it this is he?'

Kelley spoke. 'Yes, that's right.'

'Where is the Captain?' said the smaller man. 'We need to see him.'

Grant spoke. 'He was called away. Said he'd be back soon.'

Oswald sat back into his chair.

'Okay,' said the tall man, 'we'll wait. We're only observing anyway. We won't get in your way, Mister Kelley. Please continue with the interview."

Lee put his hands flat, palms down on the desk.

...all we need now is for everybody else to come back in and we can have a party...

Oswald wriggled in his chair, putting his legs out in front of him.

'Mister Oswald, these two gentlemen are Forest Sorrels, who is Special Agent in Charge of the Dallas Secret Service and United States Marshall Robert Nash. They are here as observers, but may wish to interview you at a later date or join in with this interview. I would advise you to remember your rights, which I understand have been read to you and that you do understand that anything you say may be used against you.'

'Mister Kelley,' said Oswald, 'I'd like just to say this,' Oswald paused for effect. It seemed to work, they were hanging on his every word. Their eyes lit up, as Lee were maybe going to confess, spill the beans about all he knew about yesterday's events. He smiled inwardly, wishing he could hold the moment forever.

'There is nothing I can add to what I've been telling you this past twenty-four hours or so.'

Lee looked away from Kelley and engaged Sorrels.

'Mister Sorrels. I want you to know that I am being deprived counsel. I wasn't charged with anything until late last night. I want an official complaint registered about my treatment in here. I was not allowed a shower until this morning. Nobody would let me wash or brush my teeth last night. I was awakened in my cell after being told I could rest for the night. On top of all that, I have not been able to speak with my wife since last evening. She's a foreigner, doesn't speak good English and I have no idea where she is.'

Lee prayed the sadness in his soul was not seeping out through his eyes. He took a breath before continuing.

'I have been denied legal representation. That is against my constitutional rights. I–.'

'Mister Oswald,' Sorrels cut in, 'that is why I am now here, acting as an observer. Now, I can't go dressing down or arresting officers, whoever they might be, merely on your say so. You must understand, the gravity of the situation. The Presi–.'

Lee himself cut in, standing, pointing angrily at Sorrels. 'To hell with the President! He's dead isn't he? He doesn't care any more! All we have now is the body! What about me, damn it?' Oswald smashed both his fists on the desk. 'I'm being mistreated in here!'

Nash and Grant moved over to Oswald and firmly put him back down in his chair. Lee shrugged them off, his half-clenched hands catching Grant in the stomach.

'Hold it now,' said Sorrels, 'that's quite a show, Lee. Now, let's all be calm. You say you're being mistreated. How so?'

'Like I said, I wasn't allowed to shower or wash until this morning.'

Agent Sorrels moved in front of Oswald and sat on the desk facing the prisoner. He spoke in a quiet, deliberate tone. There was no mistaking the question.

'Have they... harmed you?'

'Beat me?' said Oswald, clarifying the point. 'No. I was pushed around when they arrested me and a few things have been said to me regarding the policeman's death, but, no, they haven't touched me since the theater.'

'Your eye looks pretty bad. Maybe we oughta get someone to take a look at it.'

'It feels pretty bad,' Lee lifted his face, looking at Sorrels, 'and my back hurts too, someone thumped me pretty hard in the fight in the theater yesterday.' Oswald paused. 'But I'm not concerned by that. I just want to get out of here and I want to know where my family is. That's all.'

Sorrels was sympathetic. 'I understand all of that Lee. I

think you'll be able to talk to Marina later this afternoon. Right now, as I said before, she's being taken care of and I believe I think your mother is with her.'

Lee lowered his head, 'Okay. Thank you.'

Oswald's thoughts returned to the midnight news conference he'd given. All the reporters pushing toward him, vying for the best place near him, pushing microphones in his face, screaming questions at him, bullying him.

Most of the questions had perished in the mayhem, lost down in the viewing theater.

...viewing theatee ...has anyone picked me out of yesterday's line-ups?

Oswald's mind leapt from situation to situation.

... has Ferrie gotten away ... and what about the others ... Jack was in the viewing room amid all the reporters last evening, just before the reporters said I had been charged with the President's murder ... Jack ... Jack Ruby is still around ...

'Now, Lee,' said Kelley. 'I understand from Mister Hosty of the FBI that you have stayed a while in Russia?'

'Yes, I stayed for about three years.' Lee scratched his head.

'Do you own a rifle?' Kelley came back.

'No, sir, I don't. I did have one some years back. But I don't own one at present.'

Kelley, glancing at some papers in his hand, said, 'Did you have one in Russia?'

'No. You can't own rifles in Russia. I did have a shotgun while I was there though. Uh, did some hunting, stuff like that.'

'Where do you keep your personal effects, you know, clothes and things of that nature?'

'Clothes? At my rooming house, where else?'

'Well, do you have anything at the house where your wife lives?'

'I got a couple of old sea bags that I keep out at the Paine's.

Just some old junk in there, really. Nothing important.'

'Well, I think I'll send some of my men around there to take a look, if it's all the same to you.'

'Do what you like, you won't find anything there.'

'Where would these sea bags be, Lee?'

'In Mrs. Paine's garage.'

'Are you a member of the Communist Party, Lee?' enquired Sorrels.

'No. I'm not a Communist. I'm a Marxist. There is a difference,' Oswald stopped and lightly put his hands on the desk. 'Look, I went through these questions yesterday. Do we really need to go over them again?'

Before Sorrels or Kelley could move in with the next question, the door handle rattled, turned and was pushed forward by Captain Fritz. The door opened and Fritz entered the room, pushed past all the others in there and sat in his chair.

'Anything I should know about?' said Fritz to Forest Sorrels, who had by now closed the office door behind the Captain.

'Nothing,' answered Kelley leaning against the partition wall, glancing out in to the Homicide Bureau. 'We've been over a couple of things. We just kept going, waiting for you to return.'

'Okay then, we'll move on.' Fritz again glanced down at his notes. The pile was getting noticeably bigger.

... got a lot of reading to do tonight ...

Fritz looked up, caught Lee's eye and said, 'Why don't you tell us about your stay in New Orleans this summer?'

6

The summer of '63 was hot in more ways than one. Lee had lied to Marina about his job in New Orleans and his reason for leaving her and the baby back in Dallas. Still, there was little he could do about that now, even if he'd wanted to. The last thing he needed right now was for her to see the kind of company he was keeping in this anti-Communist hotbed.

Marina had been disappointed, though, when he had told her his apartment was near the Mississippi River, a river she had read about as a girl in Leningrad and that she wished to see sooner rather than later. His wife had a way of making her man feel like he was betraying her with every fiber of his being, that he was going to go to the river, sail upon it and generally enjoy himself.

'I'll be working most of the time in New Orleans,' he'd said, 'and I won't have the time to think about boat trips on any river. We can both go on any trip you like when I've saved the money, when you come out here.'

Soon, it would be time for Marina and June to join him but first Lee had some very important work to complete.

His cover was as a maintenance man in a coffee production company, greasing the large coffee grinding machines. To call the job boring would be an understatement, but the post covered a multitude of sins.

The William B. Reilly Coffee Company was only a stone's throw from his apartment, both being located on Magazine Street. The job had obviously been fixed for him although he didn't quite know who by and he didn't really care. The position at Reilly's gave Oswald cover, a wage and a reason to be on Magazine Street.

Lee looked across at the dirty white three storey building on the corner of Camp Street and Lafayette Place. He had walked from his apartment, west up Girod Street and turned right at the end of this block and then crossed the street. He now stood on the corner of Capdeville Street, his back against the old Courthouse.

...wonder if I'll recognize him...

Lee leant back into the shade. It was almost noon and the sun was high and mighty, blazing down on another lazy, New Orleans day.

'Wonder if he'll recognize me...' Lee muttered under his breath.

Oswald narrowed his eyes and peered out across the road. In the doorway of the white building several people were conversing, directly in front of the doors, blocking his view. Lee knew that he should be in there... had better be in there.

The sweat oozed from his arms and he felt a slow trickle of it down his back. It had only been thirty minutes since he'd gotten out of the shower and he was all but ready to climb back in to it. The perspiration was showing through his white shirt and he felt embarrassed.

...still, I suppose this kind of weather hits everyone ...

Though he had been born in New Orleans, this was his first trip back since he had left the country, enroute to his Soviet calling in fifty-nine. He couldn't remember a hotter day in all the time he'd spent here before his mother had hawked all the young Oswald brothers up to the pits of New York.

Lee pulled the front of his shirt away from his chest, cupped his lower lip and blew a cool breath up over his face. He smelt the aroma of his after shave mixed with sweat and wiped down his face, annoyingly finding a bristly spot he had missed whilst shaving earlier. He was thinking of a cool drink someplace when the man he had waited for finally appeared in the doorway. Oswald pushed himself away from the wall, out of the shadows and into the midday sun. The man conversed with the people hanging around the door of the white building.

To Lee, they looked Latin, maybe Cuban or Mexican. They were listening intently to the man as he spoke. Lee slowly pushed his head forward in an attempt to see if the man was who he thought he was.

The Latins moved away, some to the left, some to the right and Lee could now see the man clearly.

He was smaller than he remembered but then Lee had only been touching manhood the last time they had met.

It is him ...

He felt a smile touch his face.

The sonofabitch, it is him...

Oswald moved to the edge of the sidewalk, arms by his side. The man across the road was now watching the Latins as they walked away, to Lee's left.

...what the hell is he wearing on his head...

Lee stepped down onto the road. As he did so, a horn sounded and Lee jumped in fright as a truck roared past him. Lee closed his eyes from the dust from the truck and momentarily lost sight of his adversary.

The grime fell back to earth as Oswald regained his stance, balancing on the curbside. When at last he opened his eyes, the man was staring at him, a huge grin on a cleanshaven face.

The two men eyeballed one another for some seconds, barely able to cross the last hurdle of recognition, each one not one hundred percent sure...

'Lee?' said the man with the shock of red hair.

... would you look at that wig! Bright red!

'Dave? Dave Ferrie?'

The man looked either side of him and crossed the street. Reaching Oswald, he greeted him.

'Lee, you sonofabitch! Come here!' Oswald was embraced by David Ferrie. 'How long has it been now... let me think.

When was it, fifty-nine?' Ferrie put his arm around Lee's shoulder and pulled him toward the white building. Lee noticed the sweat stain beneath Ferrie's armpit and his own embarrassment dissappeared.

'Fifty-six. How could you forget that?' laughed Oswald.

'Well,' Ferrie shrugged off his mistake, 'how about that. So! You finally got back?'

... got back ...

'Uh, yeah. Got a call from Bishop last month. Told me to look you up down here. What are you up to?'

'Enough time for that later. Tell me what you've been up to!'

'Well, this and that, you know. Got married, too.'

'Well, you have been busy! Where is she?'

'Dallas.'

'Good, then we won't have any problems with bleeding hearts will we.'

Ferrie squeezed Oswald's shoulder as he guided him onto the sidewalk. 'Understand you turned into a regular little Commie on your travels, Lee! That won't do around here, you know!' Ferrie laughed out loud.

Oswald hung a limp smile on his face. 'Well, Dave, you know how it is. One minute you're this, the next minute you're that.'

'Sure, sure. Hey, listen, I'm only kidding around, Lee. You know me, always kidding around. Still it's good cover for you. Gee,' Ferrie stopped and looked at Oswald. 'You sure have grown, Lee,' he looked Oswald up and down. 'Yeah! You sure have grown.'

'What happened to your head, Dave. Why the wig?'

'Hair fell out! Getting old, I guess. Me– old!' Ferrie laughed and tapped Lee on the head. 'Anyhow, you can talk! What happened to you?'

Lee squirmed. 'Getting wise, Dave. Getting wise!'

Ferrie laughed.

The pair reached the door of the white building, Ferrie pushed it open. 'Time to meet some friends of mine, Lee. We can't stand and chat about old times forever. Time to get to work.'

*

Sorrels produced a small pile of literature and threw it onto the desk. One of the leaflets was yellow - in black it shouted 'Hands off Cuba!' The body of the leaflet contained an invitation to join the New Orleans Chapter of the Fair Play for Cuba Committee. The other, a pamphlet entitled The Truth about Cuba, published by the Fair Play for Cuba Committee, 799 Broadway, New York 3, New York. Lee recognized this printed matter as his own.

'What are these about? Can you tell me that, Lee?' Sorrels moved toward the door and leant against the frame.

Lee looked at the pile of literature almost lost in the existing mess on Fritz's desk. Reaching forward, Lee picked up several of the pamphlets and flicked through them.

'I did some work for the Fair Play for Cuba Committee in New Orleans during the summer,' he stated flatly. 'Those are samples of my stuff.'

Oswald shrugged and sat back in his chair, glancing at the eyes staring at him. Nash sat down in front of Lee, never taking his eyes from him. Oswald returned the stare, then looked away.

'We have a report from an officer,' started Fritz, 'one of Chief Curry's men, that you were giving out this kind of stuff here in Dallas back in April or around that time. Can you tell us about that?'

As the Captain finished speaking, his eyes dropped to his notes again.

'Don't really know what the problem is, Captain. I just passed around a few leaflets, that's all.'

Sorrels took up the questioning. 'Were you working with

or for anyone whilst engaged in this activity?'

'Depends what you mean. I guess you could say that I was working for a cause, a cause that means a great deal to me and a great deal to a lot of people,' Lee paused, measuring his words. 'As for actually working for somebody, then… I have to say that I really don't know what you mean.'

'Then you weren't engaged by person or persons known to you, people who may have been using you, maybe even paying you–'

Oswald interrupted Kelley's questioning. 'Look, I… nobody is going to pay someone to pass out–.'

'But you did, isn't that right?' snapped Kelley.

'In Dallas?'

'In New Orleans in the summer, we have an FBI report that identifies you and two others passing out pro-Cuban leaflets in Downtown New Orleans, outside the Trade Mart of all places. We know that you paid these two people a couple of dollars each to help you distribute your propaganda.'

'I have nothing more to say,' said Oswald, angrily. 'I want my lawyer.' Lee slammed his fist down hard on the desk. The questioning stopped abruptly. The phone rang again.

'Fritz,' the Captain stood as he listened to the caller. 'Yes. I'm on my way.'

Fritz replaced the receiver and collected his papers. Moving to the door, he said, 'Mister Sorrels, you and I are wanted in the Chief's office. If you come with me …'

Sorrels pulled open the door and let the Captain pass. 'Be right back,' Sorrels said, following the Captain. The buzz of the Homicide Office fell into the office again. Sorrels closed the door behind him.

'Lee,' Kelley continued, 'have you ever gotten permission from the Cuba Committee in New York to represent them?'

Oswald sighed.

'Yes,' he lied.

*

'So, let me see if I've got this right. New Orleans is the most anti-Communist piece of land in the Western Hemisphere and you want me to hand out pro-Castro leaflets outside the Trade Mart? If you ask me, that sounds a little crazy.'

Lee sank back into the chair in David Ferrie's office on the second floor of the white building. The massive six foot six, two hundred pound man with the closely cropped white hair opposite him leant forward and engaged Lee with bright, staring blue eyes, 'But, Lee, we're not asking you what you think about it. That's the job. That's what you were sent here for.'

Ferrie held his hand up in surrender to the big man. 'Clem, now wait up,' Ferrie turned to Oswald who was staring at the floor. 'Lee, it's ... it's a job. We need the job to be done. We need you to do it for us.'

Oswald looked at Ferrie. 'I did this stuff in Dallas last month. No one approached me, unless you count the cops who were going to throw me into jail. It's pointless. There can't be anyone in New Orleans who would tell you they were for Castro, even if they were!'

Clem spoke. 'And what do you know about this area? You just got down here from Dallas, goddamn it, so don't tell us about our own back yard,' Clem turned to Ferrie. 'Who found this guy?' he spat. 'Whose idea was he?' Clem threw his pencil onto the desk. It rolled across some papers and then fell on the floor at Lee's feet.

Lee looked at the pencil. Ferrie motioned to him to pick it up. Lee did so and then put the pencil onto the desk.

Ferrie continued as Clem looked up at the ceiling. 'Come on, Clem, this guy's okay. So he doesn't want to get punched by anyone!' He turned to Oswald. 'Lee, this job pays. On top of that, you'll still be picking up your money from the Coffee plant. What more do you want?'

Lee pursed his thin lips, glancing between the two men. Shuffling in his chair, he said, 'Bishop told me I was getting out of this kind of thing. He said this kind of stuff was beneath me. Said I was moving onto other things.'

Clem sniggered, but controlled it. 'You get real money for doing this.' The big man leant forward. 'Real money.'

Real money sounded good to Lee. A fat lip was not as attractive.

'Okay,' he said, 'Okay. But who am I s'posed to be getting at?'

Clem looked him in the eye again.

... those eyes are amazing ...

'The lunatic fringe. Anybody. Sure, some anti-Castro people will come by and not be too pleased, but that's not the point. There are some people out there who will be interested ... and they're the ones we want. We're relying on you, Lee.' Clem paused. 'The money's good.'

Lee raised his hands. 'Okay, okay, you convinced me. What exactly do I do?'

Ferrie spoke as he glanced at Clem. 'Atta boy, Lee, I knew we could rely on you. First off, you'll need this ...'

Ferrie passed Oswald a bulky manila envelope. 'Open that and I think you'll see how glad we are to have you on board.'

Lee looked down at the envelope, turning it over and over. 'Go ahead, open it.'

Oswald ripped off the top of the envelope. Opening the top with two fingers, Lee peered in.

Ferrie chuckled. 'You like that, Lee? Huh, you like that?' Ferrie pushed Lee playfully. 'Could you handle more of that, Lee?'

Oswald stared into the envelope. 'There must be–'

'Twelve hundred dollars,' cut in Clem, 'where you gonna get that kind of money for passing out leaflets?'

'But–' Oswald was dumfounded.

'Don't knock it,' said Ferrie. 'That's chicken feed. This is what Bishop was talking about, Lee!'

Oswald looked up sharply at Ferrie. His gaze met Ferrie's, grinning like the cat that got the cream. 'Yeah!' He grinned, 'That's what Bishop meant. Listen, there's a lot of shitty jobs to do out there. But the money's good, yeah?'

Oswald couldn't disagree. 'Well, yeah! Sure, uh–'

'The big league, now Lee,' enthused Clem. The big man stood up from behind the desk. Lee followed him up.

...he's a giant and no mistake ...the biggest sonofa...

'Remember, Lee,' said Ferrie, 'that's money for the whole time you're here,' Ferrie laughed, 'Not for one week's work!'

Oswald was still stunned. He'd never held so much money.

'Listen, Dave,' said Clem glancing at his watch, 'I gotta go. I'll see you later.'

Clem walked from around his desk to Lee, hand outstretched. Lee took it.

'Welcome aboard, Lee,' Clem smiled, his entire face opening up to show a full set of dull white teeth, spoiling the man's striking appearance. His high cheekbones were prominent and Lee noticed for the first time the dark heavy bags beneath Clem's eyes. The man-mountain moved to the door, but not before he and Ferrie had clasped hands and embraced each other. Ferrie patted Clem firmly on the back.

'I'll see you later,' said Ferrie.

Oswald watched Clem as the door closed behind him. Ferrie turned to Lee.

'What the hell is wrong with you,' he yelled, startling Oswald. 'What are you trying to do?"

Ferrie reached the desk and slammed his fist down hard on it. Several loose papers and the pencil fell to the floor. 'You don't mouth off that way again, y'hear? Jesus...'

The pencil rolled out of Lee's reach and into one corner. The papers fluttered in the disturbed air, taking forever to gently settle on the wooden floor. Lee sat back, even more dumfounded than when he'd first glimpsed the money, his eyes never leaving Ferrie, his nerves tingling.

Wiping his forehead with the handkerchief he'd pulled from his pant's pocket, Ferrie mumbled as he sat down in the chair vacated by Clem.

'Do you know who that guy is? What he represents? Huh?' Ferrie stared at Oswald. 'Have you any idea who he is?'

'Uh, no–'

'No? What did you say? No? Well, I can see you don't.' He wiped his face again and exhaled deeply. 'Jeez ...'

Lee sat transfixed.

... this guy is crazy ....

'Look,' said Ferrie, having regained his cool. 'I shouldn't have yelled that way.' He hung his head, dropped the handkerchief and held up his hands. 'I'm sorry. I shouldn't have yelled at you ...'

Oswald looked at the money hanging from the envelope.

... what the hell can I say to that ...

'Look, Dave, I–'

'No, no. It's me, Lee. Let's forget it, okay?'

Oswald studied Ferrie's round face. The red wig he wore was no more than clumps of material stuck to his head and for the first time Lee noticed the eyebrows were just tufts of the same, again stuck to Ferrie's face. Ferrie's long, pinched nose hovered above thin lips, Lee thought his large ears might flap in the wind. They also seemed to be glued onto either side of Ferrie's head. He looked tired, shattered and weary.

Lee noticed that Ferrie also looked very, very sad.

'Forgotten,' agreed Lee.

*

'So,' continued Kelley, moving away from the door as a uniform passed through some paperwork to agent Grant, 'you have had permission to represent the Fair Play for Cuba

Committee in Dallas and New Orleans?'

'I advised them of all my activities' he said evasively.

'That's not the same and you know it, Lee,' said Kelley, browsing through the papers that had just arrived. 'Did you get their permission?'

Oswald stood and shook his wrists, the handcuffs rattling. 'Can you take these damn things off? Where the hell am I going to run to, even if I get past you?'

Lee continued to stand. He rattled the manacles again.

Kelley looked at him.

'Okay, okay. But any trouble... Bob?'

Marshall Nash signaled for Oswald to sit and he did so. Nash gripped Lee's wrists and found the key to his bonds. Released, Lee looked at Kelley.

'Thank you,' he said, gratefully.

'Let's get on with it, Lee.' Kelley paced the office, glancing into the Homicide Office as he did so. 'The Fair Play–'

'Let me tell you,' interrupted Oswald, 'I will not answer any questions regarding any activities I may or may have not undertaken during my stay in New Orleans this summer. Let me call my attorney.'

'We're going around in circles, Lee. We're not getting very far at all. You could clear up a lot of details while you try to obtain your…' Kelley glanced at his notes. 'Mister Abt.'

Oswald became belligerent, frustration seeping through his cool exterior. 'Why don't you just let me go? I've done nothing, for Christsakes!' Lee looked up to the ceiling, sighing. 'The charges you laid on me last night are a joke! I haven't killed anyone yesterday, last week, last year or anytime!' Oswald slammed his fists on the desk again, an exasperated expression settling on his face.

'Cuff him, Bob,' said Kelley.

A look of desperation fell onto Lee's face. 'No!' he pleaded.

Bob Nash held the prisoner's wrists together while Agent

Grant replaced the shackles. Oswald struggled, but soon surrendered.

Dejected, Lee sat back into the chair, looking at the floor, feeling like screaming, not daring to reveal his deepest emotions. His breathing labored, Oswald chewed his upper lip, trying to retrieve the handle on the situation that he'd momentarily lost. Lee saw his chest rising, as if he'd been running over a great distance, heart pounding through his chest. It reminded him of his sprint to the rooming house yesterday.

The officers moved away. Lee felt like a rat in a trap, unable to convince anyone of his innocence.

... who did that guy see when he said someone ran down in front of the Depository ... no one I know looks like me ... who the hell was it?

... Ruby ... what of Jack, that fat bastard ... times running out ... I've got to start talking soon... Bishop...

Kelley moved over to his prisoner. 'I warned you, Lee. I won't tolerate any violent actions.'

Oswald looked him squarely in the eye and spat, 'Go to hell, Kelley. I know what you're doing. I've been interrogated before, by professionals, people who knew what they were doing. You're giving me the buddy treatment, I know. Elsewhere, it would be very, very different.'

He turned his head away, eyes falling to the floor.

... go to hell, you'll get nothing out of me ... not until I'm ready ... stick around though, that may not be long away ... I'll spill the lot, but not to you, you sonofabitch ... it's almost time, I'm almost ready ... do you think you will be? I may get blasted, but I'll take as many of those bastards with me as I ...

'Okay, I've had enough, too,' returned Kelley, the first time he'd spoken in anger. 'But where are you going? To a cell, is where. Me? I'll leave that for you to figure out.'

Kelley signaled to his officers. Lee stood as they approached.

With Nash and Grant either side of him, they pulled Lee to the door. As the door opened, the sounds of the Homicide Office flooded the room.

'Here he comes!' someone shouted. Heads turned, the place was full of policemen and news reporters. Lee didn't think much of the Dallas Police Department's security.

... anybody could get in here ...

Lee moved slowly into the Homicide Office, policemen and newsmen staring hard at him, the odd question being thrown in his direction.

Oswald ignored them all.

As Nash and Grant moved their captive into the corridor, bulbs flashed as photos were taken. Nash tripped on a mass of TV cable that nearly sent him to the floor.

'Damn!' he cursed, barely regaining his balance.

Oswald saw the multitude ahead of him, a myriad of expressionless faces glaring at him.

And then he saw Jack Ruby to his left, leaning against the wall, Fedora in hand.

Lee stared at him.

... get me the fuck out of here ... you hear me ... Jack, get me out of here ...

Ruby stared back, a flat expressionless look on his face. As Lee passed him, their eyes locked.

... if only my hands were free ...

Nash and Grant pulled Oswald through the mass of humanity toward the jail elevator. Lee tried to look back to see where Ruby had gone...

With the appearance of Ruby in the hall, Lee's head was swimming with frustration and anger, as he screamed silently at Ruby.

...what happened yesterday ...where are the others and why the hell are you stalking me instead of getting me out of here... and Bishop, where is that sonofabitch ... you bastard Ruby ... Bishop!

Five minutes later, he sat alone in his cubicle.

7

Lee Oswald spent the next few days in total boredom. His job at the Reilly Company was hardly the most riveting of all the mundane jobs he'd had in his short career. Still, it was cover for bigger things and the thought of another pay packet like the previous one eased the monotony. Lee hadn't seen Ferrie or Clem since the meeting either. He found himself thinking about his next encounter with the dynamic duo.

David Ferrie had changed a great deal in the six or seven years since Lee had met him, during his Civil Air Patrol days in the mid-fifties. Then, Ferrie had been the life and soul of the entire troop and all the boys in Lee's unit had felt a certain hero worship toward him. After all, how many kids were taught how to use and fire hand guns, automatic weapons, rifles with telescopic sights and, to top it all, taken up in Ferrie's own single engine Piper Cherokee for free private flying lessons?

Lee felt the admiration coming back like in the old days, as he recalled many hours in the air, wondering if the Marines could be as intoxicating as this. As a sixteen-year-old, Lee had seen only the excitement enveloping the danger, not comprehending that injury and death were a reality.

His move into languages had come as a total surprise, he only took the first test because one of his buddies had told the unit how Lee couldn't even speak English correctly. Coming second in the Spanish test had boosted his ego and his chances of an intelligence promotion after only a year in the service. Then, after he'd seen DelGado reading a copy of *Das Kapital* in Russian, it had pricked him even more.

Lee began to learn Russian. Now, six years later, staring out from his lonely second floor room, Lee Oswald could see the car parked across the street. He'd noticed the car on his arrival and presumed it was the FBI keeping tabs on a former defector to the Soviet Union. Parting the lace curtain, but standing back in the shadows, Lee could observe a pair of Feds sat patiently in the uncomfortable, balmy darkness of another New Orleans evening. Lee watched the car for hours.

Occasionally, a hooker would approach the vehicle only to move rapidly away as, presumably, the men identified themselves to the unsuspecting female.

Lee smiled.

... at least while they're watching me ...

The car became Oswald's main source of entertainment during an evening, his room not having a TV set or a radio. The room was quiet, lit only by his bedside light, its stark yellow lampshade casting a sickly glow on the walls and ceiling.

...two days 'til contact... two more stinking days to lounge around, wasting my time...

He tried to keep himself occupied by taking several books out from the local library, fortunately not far from his rooming house.

Lee let go of the lace and it fell back into place, partly obscuring his view from the window. After a lengthy pause, he moved back to his bed and sat on it. The open book by his side, *Profiles In Courag*e by John F Kennedy, had become an albatross and he had finally given in to flicking through the pages. Oswald had been trying to read the damn thing for over two days now, but he was getting nowhere with it. Lee picked up the book, folded one of the page corners and set it down on the bedside cabinet. He relaxed his shoulders back into the pillow, kicked off his shoes and settled his legs and body on the bed, staring up into the yellowish blaze on the ceiling.

... almost a year now since I got back from that shit hole Minsk ... still no real money, half a family, a wife who wants to go and live

with her supposedly high class friends in Dallas ... and George ...not a damn word in months ...

Oswald turned onto his side and rubbed his weary eyes. His depression was growing so quickly he could feel it.

... in over my head ... what the fuck am I doing in this place ... dirty work ... lousy, dirty work ...

Lee began to think of Marina and his daughter June. Up until now, he hadn't even been a reasonable husband or father. The pressures of his circumstance were building up inside of him and Oswald found himself longing for some contact with Bishop, if only to reassure him of the job he was doing.

Like the job at the NASA base.

... where am I on that ... that's surely going to turn into a little gold mine for me at some stage, but how much longer do I have to keep throwing myself into the lion's den for these people ... non-stop for almost four years now, not even a holiday of some sort ...plenty of lying around in sleazy apartments, though, waiting for God knows who to arrive...

He felt hungry lying in his gloom, but knew he dare not venture out, not tonight anyway. If the car outside was the FBI, but not agents familiar with his file, then Lee could find himself in for some nasty questioning.

Oswald cursed himself for not buying some extra food for occasions such as this, just something to stop his stomach growling into the night.

Lee sat upright on the bed, a sudden impulse crossed him.

... damn it, I'm hungry and there's a nice little joint down the street open to all hours ... so what if the FBI tail me ... hell, they can join me if they want, I could do with some company ...

Lee swung his legs over the side of the bed and planted his feet into his shoes, stood up and thrust his hand into his pocket. Finding no change he remembered that his billfold was under the pillow. He found a five-dollar bill in it. Lee thrust the money into his pocket, grabbed his jacket from the hanger on the back of the door whilst opening it. Pulling the door open, moving through it and slamming it shut behind him, Oswald crossed the landing swiftly and headed down the stairs. He walked into the street and stopped. Glancing either side of him, then moving off to his right, he glimpsed the car parked on the next block, close to the drug store. As he turned, Lee saw the headlights of the vehicle come on.

Time for some fun and games.

Oswald walked slowly up the street toward Morgan's Deli, where, the day before, he had eaten the best chilli and salad he'd had in years. That evening, Oswald couldn't help noticing, Magazine Street was strangely quiet. Usually a hive of sordid night life, there seemed to be no-one on the street but him. and the car slowly following him, several yards behind.

… here they come …

Oswald ignored the car as it pulled up alongside him. After a few steps he glanced to his left and at the car. He noticed the passenger's window was down. Lee's mind began to race and he increased his step.

… what a sap I am … maybe these guys are the local mobsters or something, maybe I'm just gonna get mugged or something …

A voice from inside the car made Lee start in fright.

'Get in,' the voice commanded, almost in a whisper.

Lee considered running.

… but where to …

He carried on walking, the car effortlessly matching him for pace.

'You heard me, Oswald. Get in.'

… Oswald … it must be the FBI … no one else knows I'm here …

The car stopped.

Lee took a deep, deep breath, opened the rear door and climbed in.

*

That Tuesday evening, Lee made his way to Ferrie's apartment. Though it was a considerable distance, Lee decided to walk there anyway. Setting off early to compensate his journey, Lee walked the streets of New Orleans for the first time in years. It was another warm evening, though a gentle breeze was blowing inland from the Gulf. Dozens of people were on the streets, all seemingly hurrying somewhere. Lee felt that he must have looked like a tourist as he wandered the red light area, the short cut to Ferrie's.

Women, men and men dressed as women all approached him. Lee was not concerned. He'd encountered similar and worse in the Philippines during his Marine tour there. It hadn't bothered him then and it certainly didn't bother him now. After all, a fight was a fight and he didn't doubt he could lay out a few fags if he needed to.

Ferrie's apartment was located just outside the French Quarter, the Vieux *Carré*, the oldest part of New Orleans, on Louisiana Parkway. A multitude of jazz combos disturbed the light breeze as Lee turned and twisted through the sleazy neighborhood and he couldn't help but notice the rare beauty in the delicate two and three tiered buildings around him. However, they did look more Spanish than French, with their high wrought iron and lead balconies, wooden shutters hiding tall and once elegant French windows.

He passed wall after wall clad in faded white paint, the odd colored doors and the old buildings falling flush with the pavement. Patios were strewn with semi-tropical flowers, fountains and shrubs.

It was quiet when Lee finally reached Ferrie's place. Having left the music and mayhem far behind him, Lee approached the spiral staircase that led up to Ferrie's second floor apartment. He paused, taking a long look around the area.

... getting jumpy ... this won't do ... after all, who knows I'm here, never mind why ...

Starting up the staircase and putting his hand on the banister, Lee disturbed flecks of paint revealing the rusty iron beneath. The flecks fell to the ground and Lee rubbed his rust colored hands and fingers together in a forlorn attempt to rid his skin of the lead fragments.

... sure could do with a lick of paint or something ...

The staircase rattled, squeaked and showed a life of its own, as if it were trying to throw him off balance. Had he been a child it may have done so and Oswald figured that any attempt to climb these stairs without forewarning the occupants of the apartment would have been in vain. The light from the only street lamp was dim, the stairway shrouded in darkness. The view up to the second floor reminded Lee of the detective in Hitchcock's *Psycho,* moving slowly but surely to his doom. A chill ran down Oswald's neck and sat on his shoulders.

... spooky, weird place to live ...

Lee moved slowly to stop the whole staircase rattling. Round and round again he climbed as he thought that the whole iron monster would collapse.

... this is crazy ... crazy ... a guy could get killed on this ... they should have one at Disneyland ...

If they ever did, he doubted Marina and June would enjoy it.

Looking down the Avenue from his new vantagepoint, Lee saw some hookers at the end of the road engaged in conversation with two young sailors. He stopped and watched them. There was some kind of argument in motion and soon, Lee could tell by the steadily rising voices, some blows were about to be exchanged, though he couldn't be sure by who to whom.

Smiling, he finished his ascent.

'Hi, Lee!' a voice came from the shadows ahead of him.

Oswald leapt out of his skin but not before he'd caught a strong hold of the iron banister to prevent him falling down the staircase. Stunned, Lee didn't make a sound. His heart was trying to get out of his chest, via his neck. The chill of *Psycho* paled into insignificance compared to this mortal danger, Lee clenched his fists in anticipation ...

'Glad you made it!' The voice's owner appeared silhouetted against the doorframe.

'Ferrie, you mad bastard, you almost scared me to death!' Lee retorted, pushing himself forward from the railing at the top of the staircase.

Ferrie, dressed in rumpled green combat fatigues, army issue boots, belt and all, looked sheepish and hurt.

'Gee, Lee, didn't mean to scare you, uh ...'

Oswald approached him, laughing. 'You stupid bastard! Get out of the way!' Lee pushed past Ferrie and walked into the apartment.

As he entered, Lee smelt the rank odor of the apartment, his face contorted, his breath taken away.

... Jeez ... what in the name of Jesus is in here ... smells like dead mice ...

Lee saw they were alone. Oswald hung up his jacket in the brightly-lit hall and waited for Ferrie.

Ferrie closed the door behind them with a quick glance down the stairwell. The white door matched the walls outside. Old, decrepit and desperately in need of a face-lift.

... not unlike my benefactor ...

'Where's Clem?' asked Oswald.

Ferrie locked the door and turned, walking past Oswald. 'This way,' he said, 'this way.'

The two men walked through into Ferrie's spacious lounge. It was probably the largest lounge Lee had ever been in and the filthiest. He walked to the middle and looked around. The place stank and looked as if it had never been cleaned or dusted. Clumps of the red 'hair' Ferrie wore lay on the floor and on the false mantleshelf, stuck together by plastic glue, empty tubes every place. It looked like the apartment had been shelled by a battleship for several days. Taking up a good portion of the lounge stood Ferrie's pride and joy.

A piano.

Lee continued his look around the apartment lounge. A large sprawling sofa to the west wall and in front of it an oak coffee table, full of magazines, untidy newspapers and more tubes of glue. On top of the papers several empty coffee ringed mugs. Oswald picked one up and looked at it.

'Don't you ever wash these things, Dave?'

'Nah, only I use them so I'm only going to catch what I already got!' Ferrie chuckled. 'You want a cup?"

'Uh, yeah, please,' Oswald doubted the wisdom of this.

On one wall, a giant map of Cuba, the Bay of Pigs clearly marked. And the Soviet missile sites near San Cristobel. Red markers adorned the map, not unlike the flight paths of attacking aircraft... or incoming missiles. Next to the map, in the corner of the room, a statue of Christ, complete with halo and people at His feet.

...weird...

In another corner stood an old, worn and dusty painting of Ferrie, dressed in what appeared to be a cassock.. Candles lay on the floor beneath the painting. On the shelf next to it, medicine bottles and all kinds of pills were scattered all around, some on the floor.

Ferrie ambled into the kitchen as Oswald continued his survey, picking up one of the magazines from the table. A green rug covered most of the floor, the coffee table legs ruffling up the center of it. The place was covered in dust. Shirts, neckties and the odd sock lay abandoned in the most arbitrary places. Lee thought he could smell something.

... sawdust ... what the hell would he be doing with sawdust ...

Ferrie's impressive library drew Lee to it.

... Gray's Anatomy ... Teach Yourself Spanish ... Math books ... Greek Philosophy... these books must be a joke ... Possible Viral Origin of Cancer by David William Ferrie . . .

Ferrie called from the kitchen. 'Lee, come and get this, huh?'

Oswald threw down the magazine before he'd even opened it and walked into the kitchen area.

'Here you go, Lee,' Ferrie passed Oswald a steaming hot cup of coffee. 'Hope you don't take sugar or anything, haven't got any.' Ferrie seemed quite embarrassed by this sudden exposure.

'Nah, that's okay.' Oswald slurped the hot beverage. 'It's fine. Uh, are those mice in that ...' Lee pointed to the corner of the lounge. He'd noticed two white animals running around in a small cage.

'Yes! I had a great idea for them, you wanna hear it?' Ferrie's glued on eyebrows twitched slightly and Lee couldn't help look at them. Ferrie seemed excited.

'Sure, tell me all about it.'

'Well, I used the mice to try and experiment on the little things, to try and find a cure for cancer. I wrote up a paper on it and submitted it to the Medical Board here in New Orleans. That done, I had hundreds of the mice left over, you know how they go at it,' Ferrie sniggered, 'so, here I was, stuck with twenty-five zillion white mice, running around the place. So I had a master plan . . .'

Oswald could feel his eyes popping out of their sockets. Ferrie was serious.

'... so, I think I might fly them over Cuba with incendiary flares attached to them, and parachute them down into Fidel's sugarcane fields and really fuck him up!' Ferrie lifted his cup to his lips. 'What do you think?'

Oswald stared at him. Ferrie drank and laughed.

... you nut case, you can't be serious...

Ferrie and Oswald moved back into the lounge. They both

sat down, Lee on the sofa, Ferrie on the adjacent chair. Ferrie put his coffee mug onto the large dining table.

'Well,' he said excitedly, 'how's it goin', what's it like to be back?'

Oswald took another drink of his coffee and put the mug on the floor next to him. 'Yeah, it's good. The coffee place gets me down though. But the guys are okay. Where's Clem?'

'Patience, Lee, patience. So, how's your kid and the wife?' Ferrie wore a slight smile and clasped his hands together on his lap, keeping his eyes glued to Oswald's.

'Oh, you know, they're good. Junie's walking now and beginning to talk a little better. Marina never shuts up anyway, I never get a word in on the phone. I'm sure I could go for a walk while she yakked on and she'd never notice,' Oswald smiled limply. He was missing Marina and Junie desperately and was finding it more and more difficult to hide it as the days went by.

'Yeah. Just hope that June doesn't talk as much as Marina, or that would be it!' Ferrie chuckled, then drank more coffee. The older man gazed at the ceiling and settled back in his chair.

Lee looked at him

... Ferrie, you're a disgrace ...

Lee glanced at the dirty clothes Ferrie was wearing, wondering when he'd last washed them. Oswald screwed his eyes slightly and thought he could see bits of dried glue just below what would have been a hairline on Ferrie's head. Ferrie's chest rose rapidly, as if he were wheezing and Lee strained his ears to hear the almost tortured breathing.

'Clem can't make it tonight,' Ferrie said sharply.

Lee was again taken aback, so sharp were Ferrie's words. 'How come?' he asked.

'Didn't say. Never does. Anyhow, doesn't matter. Our little project is on ice for a couple of days anyway. More coffee?'

Lee picked up his almost full mug. 'No, thanks, still got

this one,' Oswald held up the mug. Ferrie kept his eyes on the ceiling.

'You know something, Lee? I'm tired of all this. You know, a guy gets sick of the same routine, day in, day out.'

'Tell me ab–'

'You know, meeting the same people, doing the same things. Things haven't been the same since I left Eastern Airlines. Now there was some excitement. Yeah. Sure was a good feeling taking up one of those big birds. I kinda miss that.'

Oswald eyed Ferrie. Dave seemed to be slipping into a world of his own. Lee looked intently at him and felt more and more uncomfortable as the minutes went by.

'You know, all I ever wanted to do was fly,' Ferrie continued. 'Since I could walk all I ever wanted to do was fly. Don't get much chance now. Got my own little bird up in Baton Rouge, up at Ryan Field,' Ferrie sighed, deeply. 'Don't get up there much though. Too busy down here.'

Ferrie shuddered and his eyes dropped to Lee's pained face.

'Hey! But what is this?' Ferrie's eyes regained their sparkle. 'God, you must be bored!'

Lee forced a chuckle. 'No, uh, if you want to talk about it go ahead, I don't mind.'

'Lee,' Ferrie sat forward and lowered his voice. 'I like you, you know that? I really do.'

Oswald wanted to get out. 'Well, I–'

Ferrie stood and laughed. 'And now I've embarrassed you! What a heel, eh? What a sonofagun!'

Ferrie moved to the window and peered through the closed blinds, leaving Lee transfixed, waiting in anticipation for Ferrie's next oddball move.

'You know, Lee, there's people out there will hurt you, you know? Lots of people. They walk around looking for someone that they can hurt. Someone who's no threat or anything to them. They find 'em, then they hurt 'em. Can you figure that out?'

Oswald looked at Ferrie, still peering through the window blind into the warm Louisiana night.

'It's almost the hottest time of the year, Lee. Did you know that? It'll get to the nineties in a month or so. Did you know, the average humidity in New Orleans is sixty-three degrees? It's a weird place. Everybody's dying of the heat and they all carry bumbershoots around with them, you know, umbrellas,' Ferrie laughed. 'People's clothes become more uncomfortable than the rain. People go crazy down here in this kind of weather. Crazy.'

Ferrie let the window blind go, a sharp crack rent the air as the plastic fell back into place.

'You know, most of the tourists,' he spat the word, 'come down here and head for the pussy infested places on Bourbon Street. You been over there yet, Lee?' He turned, a large grin on his face and moved to the drinks cabinet, next to the window.

'So you watch them, Lee. You watch them,' Ferrie pulled down the lid of the cabinet and pulled out a medium sized whisky bottle and a single glass. 'You gotta keep your eye on 'em the whole time.'

... I hope he means the people, not the girls ...

Lee heard the splash and glug of the whisky hitting the glass.

'Me, I know everybody's business. It's the only way to keep your head above the shit.' He turned, raising his glass and downed the contents in one.

'Paaaah!' said Ferrie and wiped his mouth dry with the back of his hand. 'That's it, Lee. Time for you to go.'

Oswald leapt up from the sofa, mug in hand. 'When will I see you?' he said quietly, hoping Ferrie would say 'never'.

'Friday. Camp Street. Same place you came to the other day. Lunch time. Come to the office and see the secretary.

Ask her for an application form. Tell her you want to work for Guy Banister, from that office. Banister will be expecting you.'

'Who's Banister? Shouldn't you give me some more details?'

'Nah. He'll fill you in.'

Ferrie raised his hand and offered it to Oswald. 'Nice to see so much of you, Lee! Take it easy on the way back, no nipping off to see some of those girls!'

Oswald looked at the hand and put the coffee mug in it. 'See you in a couple of days, Dave.'

Ferrie smiled warmly and Lee imitated him.

'Yes, yes you will,' Ferrie moved back up the hallway to the front door and opened it. 'Safe journey back.'

Oswald sighed in relief when he heard the door slam behind him.

8

'Okay, Carlos. If you want to hit me, hit me.'

Lee smiled as the Cuban Exile, armed with his two side-kicks, squared up to punch him. Around the street where they stood were the scattered remnants of Lee's *HANDS OFF CUBA!* leaflets, kicked into the air by Carlos as he bore down on Oswald.

'You are a fake!' screamed the Cuban, ' I will finish you for this!'

Oswald frowned as he moved back a step. 'But, Carlos,' he said, 'we can work together!' Oswald raised his hands as the three Cubans approached him again. Carlos was incensed. He grabbed a passerby and screamed at him.

'See! You, look at this man! He is a traitor to America!' The man ignored the hot-headed Cuban and walked away. A crowd began to gather, some grinning, some not. Carlos tried in vain to grab another passerby. 'Look at him! An American, in support of Castro! The enemy of United States.'

Oswald began to laugh. Carlos' two companions began to rip up more leaflets and throw the strips of paper into the already heated air of downtown New Orleans. Oswald watched as the paper slowly settled onto the pavement.

'That's okay, Carlos! I'll get more!' shouted Oswald.

'You are a fake! Only yesterday you came into my store offering your services to me in the fight against Castro! You American bastard!'

The Cuban was in danger of over-heating. 'Now you say the opposite!'

Oswald said nothing and began to pick up his remaining leaflets. As people streamed by, he thrust the soiled literature into their hands, shouting, 'Hands off Cuba!'

Suddenly, the wailing of a police siren could be heard heading toward the incident. As the Cubans turned to see from where the police car was coming, Oswald grabbed Carlos and wrestled with him.

The police car screeched to a halt, its two uniforms leaping into action. In a matter of minutes Oswald and the three Cubans were in the police station being charged with disturbing the peace.

*

Later that evening, Lee sat in a New Orleans Police Department cell, a smile on his face. All had been accomplished. Ferrie's idea of getting him publicity had worked and Lee knew that Clem would be pleased, not to mention Guy Banister. The New Orleans chapter of the Fair Play for Cuba Committee was almost finished, smashed by his own hand. Their plan to make any Castro sympathisers unwelcome or accepted in this crazy town had certainly been a success. Lee felt the relief of finishing a good day's work. The pleasure of getting the work done, but still glad to be out of it. All he needed now was Marina to share in his achievement. But she was with Ruth, doing… God knows what. The thought tarnished his feelings and he began to feel somewhat depressed.

… hell, I can't even go for a beer ….

Staying the night in the cell wasn't about to worry him too much. He lay back on his cot and stared up at the ceiling, trying to raise his spirits. Many thoughts passed through his mind. Settling on an obvious one, he gave his brain a free haul.

… maybe a bonus for this … even more money for us to enjoy later… we might even end up millionaires at this rate …

His thoughts drifted to Carlos and his friends. They had played their part well and would be home by now planning more activities against the Cuban Dictator.

Lee closed his eyes and fell almost immediately asleep.

*

Guy Banister sat rumbling and red faced in his chair. In front of him stood an old oak desk, dark and chipped, covered with papers and files. The glare from the window behind him, plastic blinds hanging limp and broken, cast an eerie sheen around his frame.

He looked sixty, but was probably younger, his gray hair glowing with the afternoon sun directly behind him. A long, uneasy shadow fell over the desk toward Lee, pointing menacingly at him. Banister's shifty blue eyes rolled in their red rimmed sockets, weary from lack of sleep, fuelled by several large whiskies and endless cups of caffeine rich coffee, with a fresh pot still bubbling in the corner of the office. The bags under his eyes and the chin beneath his other chin trembled as if in fear. Even though he was almost a silhouette, Lee could still define the character traits of a former FBI agent.

Interrogation

Since being summoned to the room, Ferrie hadn't spoken. In fact, Lee noticed, the normally jocular Ferrie hadn't known where to put his face when both of them had gone through the door.

Oswald stood in the center of the office, staring directly at the wall ahead. Lee remembered his first court marshal in the Marines, having injured himself in the arm with the accidental discharge of a small revolver he'd kept in his locker. Such ownership was forbidden and he'd felt like a child being reprimanded for not doing homework when the captain had finished with him.

... this can't be as bad as that ...

Ferrie stood to Lee's left, leaning on a wide filing cabinet. Oswald had noticed the cabinet and hoped he might get a closer look at the contents some time

... if I live that long ...

Lee wanted to laugh, but dare not; he felt like a kid.

The office was quiet, even with the bustle outside. Occasionally, he could hear a voice carried on the wind and through the half open window. The traffic was not busy. A Sunday afternoon never was. The atmosphere was stuffy and Banister's love of cigars didn't help.

Banister at last stood up, meeting Lee's clouded gaze.

'So,' at last he started, almost in a whisper, placing his hands in his suit trousers, belly hanging over the belt, 'so you come down here to do some work for us, hmm?'

Oswald started to speak but was cut off by Banister raising a finger and pointing at him.

'Don't ...' Banister exhaled, trying to calm himself, 'don't even think about answering.'

The older man moved from behind to the front of his desk. Sitting on the corner, hands back in pockets, straining the material on his pants to almost ripping point.

Lee could feel Ferrie shriveling beside him.

... get on with it ...

'We run a tight ship down here, Oswald, I'll give you that for nothing. We watch out for each other,' Banister stood and looked Oswald right in the eye. Lee could feel the coldness of them, but did not flinch.

'We've been at this game a long, long time,' he turned to Ferrie and raised his voice, over Oswald's shoulder. 'That right, Dave? Been a long time?'

'Yes,' Ferrie replied swiftly, but added nothing more.

'Yes, but Dave and I here, well, we're getting older. We all get older. So, us old guys have to teach you young guys the wheres and whyfores so you can sleep easy at nights,' Banister looked sharply back at Lee and barked. 'You get me?'

Oswald looked ahead, staring at a spot on the wall, through Banister's skull. Banister turned and bent over, Oswald's eyes followed him as he rummaged about on the desk. Spreading papers this way and that, Banister finally found what he was looking for. Lee saw the yellow sheet of paper. It looked familiar, like one of the pamphlets he'd been handing out to passersby near the Trade Mart earlier that week.

Banister turned again to face Oswald. 'This,' he yelled, almost pushing the pamphlet up Lee's nose, 'is what this is all about.' He brought up Lee's hand from his side and thrust the pamphlet into it, 'This is what it's all about. Look at it.'

Banister moved away, pulling a cigar from his inside jacket pocket. With Banister now patting the sides of his jacket, searching for a light, Oswald looked down at the pamphlet. Indeed, it was a copy of the literature Lee had had printed up at Jones' Printers. He studied it.

Ferrie moved from foot to foot as he fidgeted about the room. Banister returned to his chair and lit his cigar, great plumes of smoke filling the room from the ceiling down. Lee felt he had until the smoke touched the floor and smothered them all to find the problem.

'Well?' asked Banister impatiently, cigar in mouth, fingers drumming the top of the desk.

Ferrie turned on the fan that had been standing idle on the top of the filing cabinet. The disturbed air shot forward from it, causing Banister's cigar smoke to swirl in and around itself above Banister's head.

Banister continued to look dog eyed at Oswald busy thumbing through the pamphlet.

Ferrie could see that Lee was stumped.

... what the hell does this guy want from me ...

Banister pulled the cigar from his mouth and sent a long cloud into the air and settled back in his chair. The battle lost, he said, 'Try looking at the inside back cover,' he put both hands behind his head, pushing the chair back on two legs until it rested against the wall.

Oswald saw the problem. Stamped in the back cover was the inscription:

FPCC

544 CAMP ST,

NEW ORLEANS, La.

'I goofed,' was all Lee could say.

Banister sat forward and said sarcastically. 'You here that, Dave? He says "I goofed".'

Ferrie muttered, but Lee didn't catch it.

'What the hell were you thinking about for that to happen?' yelled the angry Banister, rising from his chair. 'Are you completely nuts? You've only blown your cover, you idiot. Have you any idea what we do down here? We certainly don't support Castro! Jesus... all that planning, how the hell do you infiltrate these pro-Castro people now, now that they think your office is my office?'

Ferrie spoke. 'It's a mistake, Guy, it ...'

'A mistake? It might as well be the end of the world!' Banister threw his arms up in disbelief and sat back heavily into his chair.

... maybe it's my insurance, you sonofabitch ... my insurance from nutcases like you ...

'Listen. If anything like this comes down again, heads are gonna roll. Do you understand me?'

Banister dropped his hands and slammed them on the desk as he tilted the chair upright and came back off the wall. He glared at Oswald and then sat back into the chair and then stood.

'I'm gonna let you in on something, Lee. In almost forty years in this business I've never seen such incompetence. Do you realize what I'm saying? This is one of the most stupid things I've ever witnessed.'

Ferrie moved over to the bubbling pot in the corner and poured some coffee into a mug. Banister watched him and Lee stole a glance.

Ferrie kept his back to them.

After a pause, Banister said, 'I hope that's for me, Dave.'

'Of course,' said Ferrie, turning. 'Here you go.'

Banister took the proffered mug and set on his desk. Ferrie moved back to the door, shuffling as he did so. Oswald felt the heat moving in on him. The room was becoming more and more oppressive and he wanted to leave. Now.

'Now,' said Banister, quietly, 'that's over and done. Dave, you got something else for this asshole to do?'

Ferrie smiled and moved back into the arena, saying, 'Oh, sure. Lots of things. Clem has a couple of jobs for him. In fact, not only is he gonna be a busy boy over the next couple of months, but we got him in the local paper, on the radio and there may be a television interview for him!'

Ferrie laughed. Banister just stared at him.

'Okay,' Banister picked up the phone and began to dial. 'Now, get the hell out of here, I got work to do.'

A feeling of relief engulfed Oswald. He felt Ferrie's hand

on his shoulder and his warm breath in his ear.

'Let's go.'

Oswald and Ferrie left Banister's office and walked down the stairs to the street.

Ferrie, looking behind him, said, 'Nah, take no notice of that sonofabitch, Lee. By the way, did you write New York?'

'Yeah. I told them I was going to rent an office down here and round up a few members for the New Orleans Fair Play Committee.'

'And?'

'And they told me not to rush into anything. They didn't think I could afford the office space and that kind of thing. They sent me more leaflets and stuff, you know, the usual stuff. I think they know what I'm at.'

'How do you mean?' Ferrie glanced at Oswald as the two men reached the sidewalk of Lafayette Place. They stood together in the blistering heat, neither shaded from the sun.

Oswald shrugged as he looked around. Ferrie eyed his young protege.

'Just a feeling, you know. Anyhow, I sent them another letter saying that I have rented a place.'

Ferrie became serious. 'Well, I hope to God that you didn't give this address.'

Lee looked at Ferrie, a half grin on his face, saying, 'You know, I really don't know how to take him. Is he a nut or something?'

Ferrie screwed up his nose and slowly patted the perspiration from his face, saying, 'This damn heat,' Ferrie pursed his lips and slowly exhaled. 'Think I'll get me a job in Alaska or someplace a little cooler!' Ferrie laughed, slapping Oswald on the back, pushing him into a walk. 'Come on,' he said, 'I'll buy you lunch. The best damned place you ever ate.'

*

Oswald pushed away his empty plate and picked up the remaining piece of bread. Lee felt content. Pulling the bread apart and placing a piece into his mouth, he reached for his second glass of beer.

'You wanna lay off that stuff during lunch hour,' said Ferrie 'you'd do better with that.' He pointed to the jug of iced water in the middle of the table.

'Great lunch, Dave. Thanks,' said Lee.

'Forget it, my pleasure.' Ferrie sat back in his chair and looked out of the restaurant window. The traffic passed by aimlessly. Ferrie sipped his iced water, studied Lee's face and plucked himself a toothpick from the small collection to his right.

'Where do you think all those bums out there are going, Lee? No place. That's all, no place. They don't have a chance. And the saddest thing of all is that they have no idea.'

Oswald looked out the window and slowly chewed his bread.

'Listen,' Ferrie shuffled in his seat and licked his thin lips before leaning forward onto the table. 'I know you could use the money right now … I may have a job that could pay you a hell of a lot more than even Clem gave you the other week,' he picked at his teeth with the toothpick.

Oswald put down his beer and dabbed his mouth with his napkin. His eyes widened as he said, 'More than twelve hundred? I'm in, what do you want me to do?'

Ferrie gestured, as if in surrender. 'Now, now hold on, Lee. Don't for heaven's sake get carried away. Just relax and listen,' Ferrie slid his tongue over his front teeth before continuing. 'It goes like this. I may, or I may not, have to go away for a few days soon.'

Ferrie looked at Oswald, 'So. . . I may need something

doing.'

Oswald hung on his every word, as Ferrie sat back in his chair. Ferrie brought his hand up and half covered his mouth.

'No,no,' he said suddenly, 'it won't work. No, forget it. Forget I mentioned it.'

'But you didn't mention anything, Dave. What is it?'

'Aaah. No, forget it. Come on, time to go,' Ferrie stood and reached into his pant's pocket, his chair scraping on the tile flooring of the restaurant. 'I'll get the tab.'

Lee watched Ferrie walk to the girl at the till and pay for their lunch.

... crazy bastard, what the hell is he talking about ...

'Come on, back to work,' Ferrie moved toward the exit, Lee followed him back out into the heat stricken street. Narrowing his eyes, Lee looked up at the glorious blue sky over New Orleans.

... a beautiful place, much nicer than Dallas, not as ... mean ...

'What you thinking about?' said Ferrie. 'Come on, get your head out of the clouds.'

'You like to have your head in the clouds,' Lee retorted. 'That's why you learned to fly a plane.'

'That's exactly why I'm telling you to get your head out of it. Never did me any damn good.'

... here we go ...

'You got any idea how many hours I've put in up there?'

... no, but I figure ...

'Must be ... oh, thousands. Thousands,' Ferrie shook his head slowly. 'Never did me any good though. Just got me in trouble with everybody! Ah, what the hell. Listen, Clem should have a few things for you to do in a couple of days. Nothing major, probably just a couple of errands, that kind of stuff.'

'But what about my job? I can't keep taking the time off.'

'Don't you worry about that, that's been taken care of.

Look, don't you have to sort out getting your family re-located down here?'

'Sure, but that can wait another couple of days.'

Ferrie put his arm around Lee's shoulder and guided him down toward the coffee plant.

'Yeah, but don't leave it too long. We don't want to spoil your cover. Whether you are aware of it or not, things like that take a lotta time to work out. There are more people than you involved in all this.'

Oswald shrugged. 'Guess so,' he said.

The next few days passed as a blur to Lee. Marina and Ruth arrived in New Orleans with June and, true to his word, Oswald took all three of the women in his life on the boat trip he'd promised Marina. Visits to the New Orleans Museum and the local Zoo took up precious time from his activities but Ferrie had warned Lee about over enthusiasm, the importance of establishing and maintaining a plausible cover for his activities.

Oswald had argued that as this was a last ditch effort to get Marina and his baby back, an effort that Lee knew to be futile, he could put off any family trips for more important things.

Ferrie disagreed and got his way.

9

'You see, Lee,' continued the Captain, 'those people out there in the corridor don't care about you, d'you know that?'

Oswald sneered at Fritz.

The Captain maintained his approach. 'Why, a story is all they want from you right now and furthermore, Lee, if you don't give it to 'em,' Fritz held up his hands, ' well, they'll just make one up. So what's it gonna be?'

Oswald sat back into his chair, his mind whirling on the titbits he could offer the Captain.

...could he take it... could he take the fact that I know more about this situation than he ever will ... what would his reaction be if I gave him the entire story; the meetings in the run down hotel room in Mexico City; the identities of the snipers; Ferrie, with his wild crimson hair and stick on eyebrows; Clem, the big business man from New Orleans; Banister, everyone's favourite alcoholic racist - the only question Fritz would want to know then, is how the hell I got myself mixed up in this business in the first place!

Fritz looked weary again. Shuffling the myriad papers on his desk had obviously become the most exciting thing happening in these talks. He took off his glasses and placed them on the desk, rubbing his eyes with his left hand. Oswald watched him closely as Fritz produced a clean, white handkerchief from his jacket pocket and began cleaning his eyeglasses. Fritz glanced at his notes.

'Do you pay Mrs. Paine any form of, uh, rent or whatever, in view of your wife staying at her home?' He didn't look at Oswald, as he asked the question.

What a question at a time like this, but if it keeps them off track.

'No, we don't pay her any money,' Lee crossed his legs, bored.

... let's see if we can't spin this one out ...

'We offered, but she declined. Ruth said that Marina and the kids could stay and Marina would be able to help Ruth with her Russian language skills. It's a good arrangement and so we all gain. It works.'

Fritz replaced his sparkling eyeglasses. 'Did you have any visitors at your apartment on North Beckley?'

...that's nearer the mark...

'No. I don't know anyone in that area. I just used the place through the week whilst at work.'

'Then what did you get up to in the evenings then? You must do something…'

Oswald frowned. 'Well, I guess I'd get home from work around five-fifteen, five-thirty… sometimes I'd work over and such. Uh, let me see. When I got home, the housekeeper would have a bite ready for me and the other guests. After that, some television maybe,' Lee craned his neck and looked at the ceiling, 'I like to read. I'd go to my room, read and maybe watch the news at around nine on the television.'

'Then call it a day?'

'Yes.'

'You ever call your wife on the phone?'

'Yes, sometimes.'

'D'you ever call anybody else?'

'No.'

'Are you a member of the Communist party?' Hosty interrupted.

Oswald looked at him. 'We covered that, but no, I'm not. I am not a member of the Communist party,' he brought up his hands and slowly massaged his face. 'Listen, I'm hungry.'

'We'll get you something in your cell later,' said Captain Fritz, 'that about raps it up for me, Hosty. What d'you think?'

Hosty nodded. 'There's a couple of things I'd like to run by you, Captain, but we don't need him.'

'Okay,' Fritz turned to Oswald. 'That's it for now."

*

Lee stood at the corner of Louisiana Parkway. It was almost sunset as he admired the pink sky above. Several clouds floated directly above him. He reflected on the crazy car ride he'd shared with Clem and Ferrie earlier that week. Oswald shuddered. The journey across Lake Pontchartrain had been one of the hairiest of his life, as Ferrie drove like a lunatic to their destination.

The twenty-four mile causeway across the lake was nothing

short of spectacular. Half way across, heading north out of New Orleans, Clem had remarked that, if Lee looked around him, he wouldn't be able to see any land. Lee did so, to find this was true. Only the lake was visible and both ends of the bridge were lost in perspective both ahead of and behind the car.

Ferrie drove like a madman, the trip was obviously an important one although Oswald did not know the reason for this giant leap across so much deep, cold water and it seemed that they weren't about to tell him. Not at that moment anyhow.

Finally they reached some destination in the northern area, Lee had noticed a signpost.

Abita Springs 2 miles.

Lee hadn't a clue where they were going, but he remembered the drive lasted another twenty-five minutes past that last turn off, down a long dusty road lined by brush …

His thoughts were jarred back to the present. A car pulled up in front of Ferrie's apartment block and four men got out from the vehicle. He recognized Ferrie and Clem immediately.

What an odd couple...

Two younger men, around Lee's age, got out of the back of the car and stood on the sidewalk. One probably American, the other definitely Latin.

Ferrie locked his door and looked over in Lee's direction.

Oswald waved and Ferrie motioned him across the street. The other three men all glanced over to Oswald as he walked toward them. Clem turned and headed for the spiral staircase leading to Ferrie's second floor apartment. The young American and the Latin followed, leaving Ferrie waiting for Oswald.

...who the hell are they?

Oswald walked around the car to Ferrie's side.

Ferrie read Lee's face as he reached him.

'Worried, huh,' chuckled Ferrie, putting his arm around Lee's shoulder. 'Don't be. These are some of the guys from the camp we went to earlier this week.'

Oswald wore a frown. 'But I thought you said that they were all arrested by the Attorney General's men ...'

Ferrie and Oswald climbed the steps slowly. Ferrie spoke fast, as if this were a great secret he intended to finish before they reached his guests, by now waiting patiently outside the apartment door.

'Most of them were arrested. Weapons all gone, too. But these two turned up the day after we got back. Clem rang me.'

Oswald looked up through the metal stairwell. He could see their shoes, filthy and caked in mud and dust. They looked like fugitives and indeed they were. The young American was badly in need of a shave, his face and hair matted with sand and dirt. Lee noticed the left leg of the man's jeans had what looked like blood on them, but he didn't seem in distress. The man's jacket was ripped across the back. The Latin looked as if he were in shock and he too looked worse for wear, his jeans and denim jacket were worn, ripped and filthy.

Ferrie and Oswald reached the top of the stairwell. The two newcomers looked at Lee, their eyes sunk and sullen, a tainted aura hung about them. The Latin's mouth hung open and Lee could see his stained teeth. They looked both scared and weary and in desperate need of a bath. Lee glanced at both of them in turn, but said nothing.

Ferrie opened the door and they all followed him into his apartment.

*

'We never stood a chance.' The young American, clean and shaven now after his bath, sat in the corner away from the window, his fourth beer clutched in his right hand and a cigarette in the other. He gulped down the beer and Ferrie passed him another can as the young man took a long drag on his smoke.

'You got anything stronger than this?' he enquired, waving the cigarette around.

'No,' said Ferrie, sharply. 'That's all you get. Get on with it.'

Oswald looked at Ferrie, who was obviously bursting to say something. Lee knew Ferrie wouldn't speak until he had a clear picture of this man's troubles.

The young American's eyes glazed over and he tried to sink further into the chair. He continued, almost as if he were talking to himself.

'We'd heard that something may have been coming down from some of the guys who came in from Miami last week,' he took another gulp of his beer. Ferrie broke into another for him. 'No,' he said, 'I'm fine... we heard that Bobby Kennedy had taken action on two of the other groups in Miami a while ago. We knew something was going to happen ...'

...acting on information received ...

The young man closed his eyes. Lee looked at Clem and Ferrie. They ignored him. The Latino still hadn't come out of the bathroom.

'Anyway,' another drag of the cigarette, 'the Feds just hit us. Guns blazing. They came out of nowhere. They were well organised and had automatic weapons. There were deaths on both sides.'

Ferrie glanced at Clem. The big man walked over to the drinks cabinet and poured a large whisky. Clem passed the hard liquor to the dazed young man.

Lee watched the whisky follow the beer. The room was getting uncomfortable for Lee, clouds of cigarette smoke hung in the air. Clem moved back to his chair and sat on it, cross-legged. His massive bulk looked as if it might break the chair in two and it creaked as he settled down, his eyes never leaving Ferrie's.

'I've never seen anything like it,' he continued slowly, 'even in combat, I've never been shot at by my own side.'

...combat... surely, he's too young to have served in Korea...

'Billy,' said Ferrie, finally putting a name to him, 'calm down. You're fine now. It's over.'

Ferrie was getting emotional. Oswald sensed a father figure in Ferrie, not, it crushed him to recall, unlike the feelings he had held all those years ago in Ferrie's Civil Air Patrol. But he'd grown out of that...

'Just take it easy,' said Clem, nodding in agreement. 'You'll be fine.'

'Yeah,' replied Billy. 'I guess I need some rest. We've been keeping low these past couple of days.'

Billy sank the remainder of his whisky with a loud gulp. Reaching over, he put the glass onto the coffee table, almost missing the side of it. Ferrie half darted forward in an effort to catch it.

'Dave,' said Billy, rubbing his face. 'You got anything to eat?'

Ferrie jumped up and headed for the kitchen. 'Sure. Leave it to me.'

Oswald and Clem watched Ferrie leave the lounge. Billy's eyes closed and he sank back into his chair, falling almost immediately asleep.

Clem looked over to Lee and raised his eyebrows. 'Looks like he's out of it for a while, Lee,' Clem spoke quietly.

Lee nodded, dropping the sides of his mouth, stood up and moved to the cans of beer on the coffee table.

Suddenly, Ferrie half shouted from the kitchen. 'Somebody ought to shoot that fucking Kennedy!'

Billy's eyes flickered as his lucid sleep was disturbed by the outburst. Then, he was gone again, his head dropping into his chest.

Clem said, 'Which one? They're both as bad!' The gray haired man laughed and looked at Lee.

Oswald forced a smile onto his face. He looked back at Clem.

Ferrie continued, amid the rattling and clatter of plates and banging of cupboard doors. 'I'm serious. In fact, I've never been more fucking serious in my whole life. You know, that sonofabitch is always getting in the way ...'

Ferrie appeared at the kitchen door, leaning on the door jam. '... the whole thing.' He looked at his hands as he wiped them on the towel. 'Take the Bay of Pigs. Kennedy promised us air support, saturation bombing of the beaches at least, but he got cold feet. Well, he may have gotten cold feet, but some of Billy's pals got cold all over. Set up like that ... cut down on the beach, massacred. You'll never convince me that someone didn't tip Castro off on that one.

'Then the missile crisis last year ... do you realize how many Russians there still are in Cuba? Kennedy told that bastard Khrushchev to get the hell out of there and what happens? The bastard leaves over five thousand advisors behind. Christ, if he left five thousand there, how many do you think were there to begin with? Kennedy must know that they're still there, Christ, I do! Why doesn't he come clean and tell the public about it?

'Thanks to Kennedy's Goddamn New Frontier, America now has a permanent nuclear threat only ninety miles from its shores - approved by the White House!'

Oswald and Clem glanced at each other. Neither spoke.

Ferrie was enjoying himself, winding himself into a rage, he continued, 'right on up to today. That bastard in the White House is a Commie if ever there was one.'

Ferrie sat down on the couch next to Oswald.

'And a nigger lover,' added Clem, dropping his arms over the sides of the chair he occupied, his huge hands almost touching the floor. 'If only we could ...'

Ferrie looked at them both in turn, 'Yeah. Somebody should fix the bastard. Somebody should shoot that bastard in the head. And his brother.'

'Which one?' added Clem.

Ferrie and Clem burst into laughter, followed by a slightly startled Lee Oswald.

The room fell silent.

Ferrie fidgeting in his chair, said, 'This may sound crazy … but, I wonder if that could be pulled off in this day and age …?

Lee interrupted. 'Nah, you'd never get away with it,' he shook his head.

Ferrie looked at Clem. 'I think it could, if someone were serious enough, wanted it enough. You know, a rifle, a tall building,' Ferrie sighed and settled on the couch. 'Somebody with enough balls,' he laughed, 'what about Billy boy here?'

'Now you are joking!' said Clem. 'He's had it. Look at him.'

Billy was in a deep sleep, probably the first he'd had since the raid.

'You know, that kind of operation would take a hell of a lot of money,' said Lee thoughtfully, 'and a special kind of person to do it. Can't be many who'd be interested, never mind be able to do it.'

'Lee's right,' said Clem, rising from his chair and walking across the room to the drinks cabinet again. He picked up a glass and turned to his two colleagues. 'You want some of this, Dave?'

Clem held up the half-full cut glass whisky decanter.

'Yeah, make it a big one. This kinda talk gets me going …'

Ferrie reached up and wiped beads of sweat from his brow with the towel and then ran the flat of his hand over his bright red wig, dried glue falling onto his shoulders like imitation dandruff. Ferrie stank, the sweet smell of perspiration reaching Oswald's nose.

Lee watched him and swallowed hard.

Clem poured the whisky, the gentle rattle of the decanter and the deep breathing of Billy the only sounds in the room.

As Clem turned toward them, he said, quietly, 'Kennedy has been stopping us getting at Castro since the day he walked into the White House. I think Dave's right. If we can't get Castro because of Kennedy, it makes sense to take care of the problem, the reason we can't get to Castro.'

'Crossfire,' said Ferrie.

Lee looked over at him, sipped his beer and said, 'Now you're talking stupid, Dave. How many people would you need for a crossfire?'

'Well, a minimum of three teams ... maybe two is all you would need. There'd only be one chance of getting a sonofabitch like the President. A clean hit the first time would be essential.'

Clem handed Ferrie his drink and sat down again.

'What about co-ordination?' said Lee. 'How many other people would you need?' He shook his head, peering into his can of beer. 'Already we're up to six, maybe ten people. Somebody is bound to talk.'

'Yeah, you're right, Lee,' Ferrie looked down into the bottom of his glass, deflated. 'It's just crazy talk, wishful thinking and all that.' Ferrie emptied his glass, downing the whisky in one.

Clem's face split with a wide grin. 'Listen to the two of you! Talking about removing our beloved President and then cussing because you can't think who'd pull the trigger for you or how many suckers you'd need to do the job! If there is an alternative, ruining him in some other way, then that is the road to go. What about his womanising? The bastard can't keep his paws off the ladies. We certainly don't need the kind of heat that would be generated by an assassination. I mean, shooting the President, for God's sake!'

'Who's to say he'll be re-elected next year anyway? He's not really doing anything, just sounding like he will,' Oswald said.

The big man laughed. 'Listen, I'm out of here ... you want a lift, Lee?'

Oswald looked at Ferrie. Ferrie said, 'Go ahead. There's nothing more we can do tonight. I'll see you tomorrow.'

*

Oswald looked around the basement line-up room again. It was here, only hours before that he had given his one and presumably only appearance before a world wide television audience. This time, however, he sensed a more sinister state of affairs. Now, instead of standing in front of the screen and the anterior of the stage, Lee found himself behind it and on it.

He recalled the day before being pushed and shoved into a line-up. An appearance that seemed totally unjustified at the time, but with the passing of hours, a dim light was beginning to dawn in his confused mind. Since the bombshell of being arraigned for the President's murder, never mind that of the policeman, Oswald had begun to feel the net of betrayal tightening around him. Though confused, he was steadily forming a plan in his head that would, should, get him out of this predicament.

The charges, he knew of course, were preposterous. Proving that would take him time, time that he could only win when he contacted Abt, sat somewhere in New York probably blissfully unaware that the President's accused assassin was trying to get through to him. The fact that Chief Curry had personally supervised Lee's own call to Abt was enough to stop Oswald thinking the Dallas Police were stalling his calls.

All that aside, Lee found himself stood waiting along side the line-up screen obviously about ready to be told that he should join in the latest charade.

'Stand here,' said the uniform in charge of him. Oswald looked at the officer, who was by now peering down the area on the stage side of the screen.

Must be about forty years old, married, three kids, one hundred and ninety pounds, rented house...

Lee found himself playing games in an effort to keep his mind alert. It was the only way he knew, forcing himself to observe all that he could of the happenings around him.

...haven't seen him before, must just have come on duty. Neat hair, must be an old serviceman, police stations always become graveyards for ex-servicemen but not much chance of me getting a job here - policemen and security guards; all that training, jumping out of planes, learning to be a paratrooper only to land up in a squad car and everybody hating your guts.

'All right, Oswald,' said the cop, catching Lee's eye. 'Up you go.'

The policeman pointed Lee in the direction of the stage steps, stood back and folded his arms.

Lee, of course, knew where to go. As he climbed the steps, he couldn't help wondering what the person on the other side had been told about him, or what he was in the line-up for...

... maybe it's not me they're looking for, maybe it's for some unrelated crime ... fat chance ...

Oswald climbed the steps to be greeted by three strangers.

Lee was aghast to see that the others in the line-up with him were not dressed in the same manner as he and that none of them looked the remotest bit like him. They were not even similar to him. One, a Mexican looking man with big, sad, brown eyes, a long drooping moustache and half a week's stubble on his face was dressed in faded blue denims, a white singlet, brown, scuffed cowboy boots and must have all of thirty years old.

...all he needs is a poncho and spurs...

The other two individuals were obviously teenagers. They, too, were not dressed the way Oswald was, Lee wearing his black pants, white singlet and black shoes. The first kid had a crewcut, bright blue eyes, was about six feet tall, wore a white jacket and sneakers.

... and the other kid has blond hair, for God's sake ... and those hands, he isn't even cuffed ...

None of them looked his way as he made his way to join them. Another police officer approached him, angrily rebuking Lee for stopping at the end of the line.

'What the hell you doin'?' shouted the big cop, red faced, out of shape. 'Get your ass over here!'

The policeman took hold of Lee's shirtsleeve, pulling him across to the NUMBER 2 position. Pointing his finger at Oswald, looking him straight in the face, the policemen said sternly, 'You just get outta line, boy, just one time, and I'm gonna make you wish you'd never been born!'

... asshole ... just like my old Drill Sergeant in the marines ...

Oswald nodded and stood in the position the uniform had told him.

'Okay,' said the officer as he walked down the steps, the clicking of the metal tips of his shoes echoing in the room. 'You all keep nice and quiet, keep still and this will be all over pretty soon.'

... keep quiet ... keep still? Well, I guess it's time to do something in my defense ...

Oswald spun on his heel and faced the wall. Anyone viewing him would immediately see this and point him out.

...this will ruin their little game ...

'Number two!' shouted the cop. 'Turn around and face the front, if you know what's good for you!'

Lee stayed where he was. His face was battered and the others he was with had no obvious markings on them, that in itself would give him a higher profile than the rest.

'You sonsofbitches!', yelled Lee at the top of his voice,

'you're trying to railroad me!'

The cop came onto the stage and pulled Oswald around to face front.

'What the fuck is your game, boy?' The police officer said through gritted teeth. 'I warned you…'

Oswald ignored him.

'You can't treat me this way! I've done nothing wrong, putting me in here with these teenagers!'

The cop pushed Oswald into the wall.

Lee replied with, 'You can all see this! They're tryin' to railroad me!'

Oswald rattled his handcuffs and walked up and down. The other three 'prisoners' remained calm, looking ahead at the screen. Lee knew somebody was on the other side of that screen, somebody looking at him.

'You're all sonsofbitches!' he yelled. 'You're tryin' to railroad me!'

The line-up ruined, any worth lost, the policeman reappeared and pulled Oswald off the stage, quickly joined by a colleague.

… well, that spoilt that little farce … they'll never be able to use that in court …

As Lee was dragged away, the Chief appeared at the door of the viewing room. Oswald saw him and gave him a taste of what his men had had.

'You're trying to railroad me, you sonofabitch, but it won't work!'

Oswald pointed his finger accusingly at the Chief. 'I know my rights! That was an illegal line–up and you know it!'

Oswald tried to prevent the two officers taking him out of the room. He slid his feet on the wooden floor, trying desperately to be heard by all who may be there.

'You can't do this to me! I'm innocent of these charges! I vehemently protest these charges! I want my lawyer.'

The Chief looked on as the officers pulled and pushed

Oswald cursing and resisting toward the open jail elevator.

'You can't do this...'

The prisoner and his guards at last were in the elevator. One of them looked over at the Chief.

Chief Curry motioned them upstairs and the elevator door slammed shut. As the elevator began to rise, Oswald caught a last glimpse of the Chief 's expressionless face through the small, meshed window of the elevator door.

Two minutes later, Lee Oswald was dragged and pushed down the corridor, back through the Homicide Area and into Captain Fritz's office. Newspaper and television reporters lined the route once again, their uncompromising attitude only heightening Oswald's chagrin.

He glared at them now with the same contempt he'd mustered for those in charge of him. His troubles highlighted by his incarceration and feelings of frustration, his wife's predicament not helping matters any.

Just what are they doing here?

His captors walked him briskly out of the elevator, not allowing him to stop and converse with the reporters.

Why has nobody asked me about Ferrie and the others?

Thoughts of treachery were forming in his mind, but still, he refused to let them settle. The people filling the corridor did not seem to heed his cries for help, nor ask the relevant questions. The media were still as stunned as he was, as the police were, as everybody was following the assassination of the President.

Looking bleary eyed, wave after wave of reporters jostled for key positions in the dimly lit corridor, arc lamps pointing at the jail elevator entrance and the Homicide Office doorway.

Questions were fired at Oswald but became garbled in the mayhem. And, as he sought to answer, he was pulled along at breakneck speed and the moment would be lost forever.

'Mister Oswald, did you kill the President?' someone

shouted at him for the millionth time that day. But, before he could give any new variation on it, he would be pulled away by the police. It was becoming an increasingly exhausting effort to slow the police down so that he might fire back some answers.

Two detectives followed behind as Lee walked quickly down the corridor, the police pushing him to the door side of the wall, forming a human barrier between him and the reporters.

'Oswald, did you fire that rifle?' A reporter shouted and as Lee turned to his left to answer the question, he caught sight of a microphone hovering in mid-air above everyone's head.

The detectives squeezed their grip on his upper arms as he tried to slow them down.

Though angry, Lee spoke clearly and to the point. 'I don't know what dispatches you people have been getting, but I emphatically deny these charges...'

Lee lifted his hands to show them his handcuffs.

As they neared the Homicide Office and the reporters closed in on the tiny ensemble, the police detective to Lee's front stopped and took a key out from his jacket pocket and began to unlock the door.

Another reporter shouted as Oswald was manhandled through the door into the Homicide Area.

'What about Connally, did you aim at Connally?'

Lee was through the door and heading for the Chief's office. Desperately, he fought against his captors and managed to turn and shout back through the open door to the reporters, by now pushing their way to him from in the hallway.

'I have not committed any acts of violence ...'

Then the door was slammed shut and locked. As Lee again headed for interrogation, he looked down at the floor and an even deeper depression began seeping into his soul, a desperation that he dare not let the policemen in charge of him observe. The commotion from the other side of the door faded and Lee wearily sat down in his corner of the Chief's office, sat back in his chair and looked up with a renewed expression of defiance written over his face.

Come and get me, you bastards. Here I am. Come and get me…

*

Lee held the phone to his ear and waited. Eyes darting about the sunlit office, he wondered how long it would be before Banister returned from the bank. Lee turned and faced the intriguing set of filing cabinets against the wall, the same ones he noticed when he'd first been in the office with Ferrie and Banister. He took a step forward, as far as the old and twisted telephone cord would allow and began to read the labels atop each drawer.

… sonofabitch … I don't believe it … he's only left the damn key in there, the damned files are waiting to be …

Oswald read the clearly marked file headings.

CENTRAL INTELLIGENCE AGENCY

… Interesting …

AMMUNITION AND ARMS

FAIR PLAY FOR CUBA COMMITTEE

… sonofabitch. I wonder if I'm in there …

CIVIL RIGHTS PROGRAM OF JFK

ANTI SOVIET UNDERGROUND

The listings went on and on. Lee looked around at the door, trying to see if Banister might have rumbled him and was watching him through the frosted glass of the wooden door.

'Lee, where the hell is he?' said the impatient voice on the other end of the phone line. Oswald pulled it sharply back to his ear.

'Oh, Dave …' said Oswald, still straining to read the contents of the filing cabinet, '…uh, he's not here right now, said something about the bank, uh...'

Lee heard Ferrie curse and then silence.

'Uh, what do you want me to do?'

... I want to get into Banister's files, before he gets back, not converse with you ...

'Dave...' Lee frowned and wondered if Ferrie might have died.

'Ahh,' he hasn't, 'no... leave it. Leave him a note. Tell him I rang and I'll call him tomorrow.'

'Where are you?' enquired Oswald, still frowning.

'I'll call him tomorrow.'

Click.

The line went dead and Oswald looked at the receiver before re-placing it. He crossed the room to the filing cabinet.

... now, all I need is about ten hours ...

Another quick look at the door, then Lee turned the key and tried the top drawer.

It slid open.

... nice and easy ...

B-70 MANNED BOMBER FORCE

... come on ... come ... on ...

He held his breath and glanced at the door. Sucking on his lower lip, Lee gently pulled the filing drawer.

... come on baby ...

Oswald pulled out the file most interesting to him :

FAIR PLAY FOR CUBA

He glanced at the door again, wiping the perspiration from his brow.

... be cool now, take your time ...

Opening the file at the first page and laying it down on the top of the filing cabinet, Oswald heard a door slam in the secretary's office.

... shit ...

Lee quickly put the folder back into the drawer and closed

it quietly, turning the key until he heard the lock tumblers go back into place, then pulled the drawer to see if it were locked.

It was.

Oswald moved quietly back to the phone and picked it up, as if using it.

... who ...

No one came in. Lee then saw somebody pass the frosted glass of the office door, move down the stairs and heard the door slam again. He put down the phone and moved to the door, opening it and peering into the cool gloom of the corridor. Looking both ways, he could see no one.

... damn ...

Lee moved back into the office and unlocked the cabinet a second time. Now, he had regained some nerve, time to dwell on the situation had only served to increase his adrenaline and he was determined to succeed.

He may never get another chance.

Opening the FAIR PLAY FOR CUBA document again on the top of the filing cabinet, Lee pulled his tiny Minox camera from his pant's pocket. Carefully, he positioned himself over the documents, quickly yet professionally focusing on the material, exposing their contents on the tiny microfilm. As he photographed the many pages, keeping a sharp ear on the activities outside, Lee smiled as his trusty camera went about its delicate work.

... nice little camera this, glad I kept it when I got back from Russia ...thought it may come in handy sometime...

That file finished, Oswald guessed he'd have enough frames on his film for maybe two more files. Quickly, glancing yet again at the door, he opened another.

ANTI SOVIET UNDERGROUND

... sounds interesting...

Oswald put the files back into the cabinet when he had finished copying them. The office, he was almost convinced, was getting hotter and more uncomfortable by the second.

The second file finished and put back, Lee pulled another.

CENTRAL INTELLIGENCE AGENCY

He opened the dossier and began to look through it, losing valuable time. He was becoming over-confident, reading the pages instead of copying them.

...Guatemalan air bases... medical supplies for... Castro... what the hell ...

At that moment, Oswald's worst nightmare suddenly became a reality. Downstairs, he heard the door slam shut and above it, Banister's voice.

Lee panicked and dropped the contents of the file onto the floor, papers spilling everywhere. Crouching, picking up the papers, putting them back into some kind of order seemed to take forever.

Oswald was sweating profusely by now. He kept glancing at the door, knowing Banister must be on his way up the few stairs to the office. Lee knew if Banister caught him in here he was a dead man.

Oswald froze as a figure appeared at the door. He had no chance of putting the folder back in the drawer, much less locking it.

This was it.

... damn ... I should have brought my thirty-eight ...

Lee's throat went dry, his senses rushing him, nerves jangling.

Suddenly, as the doorknob rattled, a voice from down the stairs called up to Banister. The figure moved away Lee, holding his breath, didn't waste his chance. The papers went back into the file and it into the drawer of the cabinet.

He locked it.

Oswald closed his tiny camera and plunged it deep into his pants pocket and wiped his brow, blowing cold breath upward and pleasantly over his face. He moved quickly to the desk and again picked up the phone, waiting for Banister's return.

Picking up the receiver, Lee held it to his ear and half waited for the door to open.

Banister reappeared, rattling on the doorknob.

As it did so, he said, 'Yeah, of course I'll pass on that message for you, Dave ...'bye,' and put the phone down.

'What the hell are you doing in here?' Guy Banister boomed as he charged through the door. 'You have no right to be in here!'

Lee turned to face a rather red faced and drunk Banister. His eyes were ablaze, the jowls on his cheeks quivered and he appeared to be wrestling with imminent heart failure.

'The phone was ringing ...' said Oswald quickly pointing to it and moving away from Banister.

Banister wasn't impressed. 'The hell it was, who let you in here?'

'...and Mrs. Roberts wasn't around, so...'

'Who the hell was it?' Banister had reached his desk and thrown some cash bags and papers onto it.

'Dave Ferrie, he said he'd call you again tomorrow ...'

Banister bent forward with his keys and unlocked his right hand drawer. As he pulled the drawer open, the keys jangled in the lock. Oswald watched him and then found himself staring down the barrel of a .38 revolver.

'You know what this is, Oswald?' Banister threatened, his gun hand trembling slightly, a look of complete madness on his ruddy face.

Lee tried to swallow, then again felt the dryness of his throat.

'Sure,' he said through unmoving lips.

'Then get the fuck out of my office and don't let me catch you in here again. Understand?'

As Banister glared at him, Lee could just see the bullets in the metal cylinder. The hammer of the .38 was cocked, straining ...

...neat ...

Lee dared to think.

... own little arsenal in his desk. Those files sure must mean something to this sonofabitch ...

Oswald nodded and moved slowly backward to the door, his eyes never leaving the end of that barrel.

*

Ferrie's air conditioner rattled and chugged in a forlorn effort to reduce the heat and humidity of his apartment. Since the previous meeting, he had obviously been doing some overdue spring-cleaning. Lee's head was buzzing. It was two weeks since Ferrie, Clem and he had, jokingly he thought, spoken about murdering President Kennedy. Now, back at Ferrie's apartment, he was again sat with Ferrie, Clem and several newcomers going over what seemed to him like a pretty well worked out plan of execution. The American he'd met at that meeting, Billy, was also there as was the Cuban who'd stayed in Ferrie's bathroom. Two other Latinos sat either side of Ferrie, listening to his every word.

... Jeez ... what have I stumbled into here ...

Ferrie sat forward, forearms resting on the coffee table in front of him. The scraps of paper on the table bore Ferrie's hand drawn diagrams and he was busily drawing even more.

Billy was smoking again, cigarette after cigarette and the air in the room was stale and choking.

'So,' began Ferrie, pausing just long enough to take a sip of his coffee. 'What we have is a nice neat plan. It's only sketched out at this point, but, with a few refinements we could be in business,' Ferrie looked up from the papers and looked at them all in turn. Picking up his coffee again, he asked, 'Any problems?'

Billy spoke, 'What about the cops? If someone sees

anyone...'

'Yeah, that's difficult. But then, so is the whole job,' Ferrie paused again. 'There must be a way around it.'

Lee spoke for the first time. 'Sure, there must be enough crooked cops in the world but shooting the President? What could possibly be in it for them, if you found them, what would motivate them to let something like this take place on their ground?'

One of the Latinos spoke, 'He is right, of course. It is not a matter of how to get to the President, but of how to escape after killing him,' the Latino smiled and raised his hands. 'I am willing to shoot Kennedy this morning ...but I am not willing to die doing it!' He shrugged and sat back into the couch.

'Simple,' Ferrie broke in. 'All we need is a scapegoat, a patsy. The police will pick someone up almost immediately, just to show the public that they're onto the job. All we have to do is set someone up to take the heat. Let's face it, even if the guy gets out, we'll be away from the area, home and dry.'

'You make it sound so easy,' interrupted Billy. 'I'm not convinced it would work. How many teams would we need? One would not cover it. If that one team were caught, we'd never get near Kennedy again. But, the more people you have in the scene, the more chance of someone talking. We would need good people too, not a bunch of fakers. Then, having recruited them, getting the President isn't the difficult part, it's the escape that's the problem.'

Ferrie's eyes opened wide. 'Maybe we could compromise some cop or someone and use that to our advantage. Maybe the cops themselves could drive us away from the area in a squad car...'

...Ferrie is adamant about this ... this is getting serious ...

'Another big problem would be the locale,' Clem spoke. 'That's something that would need to be looked at carefully. A high building or hill would be the best bet, but where?'

'What about money and weapons?' said the Latino nearest the window. Oswald looked at him and recognized him as the man who'd stayed in the bathroom during the first meeting.

'I don't really see weapons being a problem. We have people for that. We can get a million rifles. As for a location, down here would be best, you know, some southern nut!'

Ferrie drank more coffee. Lee noticed a change in atmosphere. All were serious about this, but none more than Ferrie. Oswald had witnessed that look in Ferrie's eye before ... the last time he'd been at the training center, north of Lake Pontchartrain, as Ferrie squinted down the telescopic sight of a Mauser. These men, these misguided misfits, were plotting the downfall of the United States Government. The situation was so unreal, so bizarre, that Oswald had difficulty taking it all in.

Lee weighed up the situation rapidly.

If this were more than just a sick joke - should I tell Bishop?

'There is a fundamental need for cross fire ... it's the only sure way of achieving a kill. You are all aware of that, that's why we need at least two snipers, two teams. One would be in position ahead of the President and one behind. It really is a simple as that.'

... as simple as that ...

'Then, someone to take the heat. Not anyone though ... the police would need to investigate this person for a few hours, while we made good our escape.'

Lee leant forward in his chair and looked directly at Ferrie.

'That'll take some checking out. If we set someone up, it'll take someone with the kind of background that would keep the cops interested enough for us to get away-'

Ferrie cut Oswald off at the knee, 'That's what I said,' he spoke contemptuously.

Oswald shriveled.

... talk about crazy ...

Billy broke in, '...and it should have been done after the Bay of Pigs.'

Oswald checked him out. Billy looked different from the previous meeting; he was clean-shaven, wore a suit and tie. Quite respectable, yet here he was, discussing, coldly and rationally, assassinating the leader of the free world.

'You Cubans have got no guts,' Billy spat, as he looked over at the Latino near the window. He pulled another cigarette from his pack.

... so, they're Cubans ...

'This guy was always gonna to let you down, was never gonna let you get Cuba back,' Billy's lighter clicked, he lit the cigarette and inhaled. 'The man speaks of peace and all that bull. Peace is fine, but not commie ruled peace.'

The others stared at the outspoken Billy, taking another long drag on his smoke. He stared at his Cuban colleagues as blue vapor trailed up to the ceiling. Ferrie gushed at him in admiration, the Cubans with a mixture of accord and hate, were obviously stung by his attack on their failure to fix the problem. Latin tempers were rising, Lee could feel it.

'He's right, you know,' said Ferrie, quietly redressing the balance and taking control of a potentially ugly scene, 'and now is the time to amend the record. This can be done and I believe it should be. I don't see money being the main problem, Clem, we both know that.'

'What do you think, Lee?'

Oswald tried not to show his true feelings.

... I'm involved now, whether I agree or not, it would be dangerous not to go along with them ... what in hell's name do I say ...

All the group looked at Oswald. Ferrie, calmly drinking the last dregs of his coffee, Billy almost finishing his cigarette and the cold, dark gaze of the Cubans fell onto Lee's face. He felt uncomfortable sat with these renegades who were intent on murder, willing to sacrifice some innocent for their bloody cause.

... Jesus... a foot wrong here and I'm dead... I'll have to tell Bishop... or somebody ...

Oswald leant forward into the breech, calculating his words, leaving no hint of betrayal in his voice.

'I agree,' he said finally, 'count me in.'

9

So Marina wants to leave me and go live with Ruth and her upper class friends in Dallas. Well, to hell with her, she can go. Can't impress on her enough as to why I need to stay here in New Orleans. How do I tell her I'm up to my eyes in a plot to kill the President; how could she cope with that, stuck here, with little or no money. The money Dave gives me, hell, I can't even spend it! More of the god-damn stuff than I've ever seen and I can't buy my daughter a lousy pair of new shoes... and the job at Gentilly ... what's Bishop doing about all this... I tell him what's going on and all he says is 'keep up the good work', well what about me... crackpot Ferrie, running around working for God knows who all the time, I tell you ... up to his neck with everybody who's not worth a damn in this town... and those crazy exiles of his... Jesus, to think I'd get mixed up with people like that... wonder if anyone else in the group knows who I am ... Ferrie can't or I'd be dead by now... four rifles with mounted 'scopes... iron sights for one of them ...

Jesus, it's warm in here. Iron sights, clip fed semi-automatic rifles, one Mauser with iron sights - I'll miss Junie if Marina leaves ... still for the best ... and Ruth... not had a holiday for four years ... maybe Russia was a holiday... and Ruby, gunrunner, narcotics, women ... lousy pimp ... Jack Ruby, the man to see ... who was it said Ruby was FBI? Nah, nah. Jeeps too...

Where do you park three hundred army jeeps ... who drives them all if they need delivering someplace ... must be out in the desert ... rifles mounted with 'scopes ... shooting at tin cans in Lacombe, Louisiana ... and Miami ... Miami is the key ... that paradise for

Cuban refugees and heroin... Miami stinks... all of it... in the wrong business... guns and drugs and girls... Bobby Kennedy closes more exile camps... but he doesn't know Miami is the key... the key to all of this...

Lee's head spun and spun. A million thoughts invaded his tired head as he lay on the sofa in the cool of his apartment. Marina and June were asleep in the only bedroom, Junie in a make shift cot Ruth had brought and left.

Lee, wearing only his pants, gazed up at the ceiling, hands behind his head, pondering his fate and that of his family.

For too long now, I've let everybody push me around and I'm sick of it ... from being born to the Marines to Russia to back home everybody gets a fair shake except Lee Oswald ... except me ... well, no more ...

Oswald peered into the gloom, his trance disturbed by the cars roaring past his window, some chased by police black and whites, singing drunks walking past, shouting hookers following them.

His breathing was labored and he suddenly felt aware of it, making him feel on edge, like his life were ticking away while he lay.

That NASA job in Gentilly ... hopefully, later, a move to Houston, Texas for real work on the Moonshots... pay must be good... Jeez, what wouldn't I give to move there now, right now... just the four of us...

Lee smiled as he thought of his daughter, June.

What a life already and she doesn't know it ... born in Russia to an American father, she's been on planes and ships, trains and cars and buses and halfway around the planet, lived in the most opposite cultures there are and all before she was barely a year old ...

Oswald sat up and tried to see through the clock on the bureau through the darkness. He could not so, after wiping his tired face, Lee got up, donned his socks and crossed the room.

Five-forty-five.... Jeez, just what I need ... another sleepless night!

He stretched and stifled a yawn.

...at least I'll see the dawn rise ...

Lee moved quietly into the kitchen.

... who the hell designed a room this small ...

He moved to the stove and glanced around for the matches, found them and lit it. Filling a pan with water, he put it on the flame.

'Lee?' Marina's drowsy voice quietly crept up behind him. 'Lee, is that you?'

Oswald turned and headed into the bedroom, saying softly in Russian. 'Shh, Marina, you'll wake the baby,'

Oswald saw June in a heap at the bottom end of her cot, oblivious to the world.

He reached Marina and knelt down beside the bed.

'Oh, Lee, did you not sleep again?' Marina's deep green eyes shone in the darkness, the dawn light from the gap in the drapes catching their beauty. She wetted her lips, delicately.

... your eyes are so beautiful ...

'No, Marina. Not too well,' Lee answered, sheepishly. He looked at her with a great sadness in his face, desperate to leave this place. The danger that enveloped him may also touch his young family.

Marina pulled her arms from under the covers and held her husband's hands. 'Why don't you sleep? Why don't you tell me what you have on your mind?' She looked at him, puzzled at his dilemma, keen to share it.

Marina pulled his head to hers and kissed him. Lee framed her face with his hands, 'I'm okay, really Marina,' he lied.

...but how do I tell you that I know some people who are planning to kill our President, people who will stop at nothing to achieve their objective and how do I explain that I am involved in a plot to change world history ...

'Just a bit uptight, you know...' Lee's voice trailed as the enormity of the plot came to the forefront of his mind again.

Oswald looked at her and he saw his wife hopelessly trying to reach his innermost feelings. He knew she would be leaving him soon, probably to return to Ruth and Dallas, back to all her Russian émigré 'friends.' Lee melted as he gazed down on her, he didn't want her to go, not now, not ever.

Marina looked deeply into his eyes and whispered, 'I love you, Lee. We will be all right, you'll see,' she smiled and pulled him to her again, wrapping her arms around him. Marina didn't see the tears well in Lee's eyes as he buried his face in her neck, feeling the softness of her flesh and smelling the musk of her sleepy body.

'Now,' she comforted him. 'Come into bed before the baby wakes ...'

*

'That's it, there...'

All eyes set on the road sign.

'McManus? Is that it?' said Ferrie slowing the car to almost fifty miles per hour. 'Are you sure?'

'I'm sure,' said Banister impatiently, 'I've got the goddamn map here in front of me.'

Lee Oswald sat in the back of the black Cadillac, thankful that he didn't drive a car and grateful for the car's air conditioning.

... it must be ninety degrees out there ...

'Okay, okay. We don't want a wrong turning here.'

'Go straight ahead, then hang a right just before McManus. We'll go the scenic route. The Clinton turnpike isn't listed, so watch out for it. Shouldn't be more than a couple of minutes drive from there.'

Banister folded the map, laid it on his lap and rubbed his weary eyes. Oswald sat silently in the rear, waiting for his final briefing. Oswald watched as Banister pulled out his cigar case and lighter.

Ferrie kept his eyes firmly on the road ahead and stepped

on the gas. Sixty, seventy, eighty miles an hour.

'Hey, you idiot,' snapped Banister, irritated by Ferrie's obsession with speed. 'It doesn't matter how much gas you give this goddamn thing, it won't leave the ground.'

Oswald smiled.

'Hey, listen,' retorted Ferrie, 'who's driving anyway?'

The two men bickered with each other. Oswald wondered if Banister was a fag, but dismissed the idea. He was pretty sure that Banister had something going with his secretary, Mrs. whatevershewascalled, sat doing the typing for Banister back in New Orleans.

...another of those damn 'don't know where I am jobs' ... why the hell all the secrecy... all this way for Christ's sake...

Banister finally turned to his left.

'Lee, look, we're nearly there. You know what you have to do?'

Oswald opened his mouth to ask a question and Banister answered before he could utter a word.

'We're gonna park outside the Registrar's Office. These niggers down here are trying to get their names on the voting list. That isn't going to happen. All we're gonna do is try and disrupt the proceedings a little. When those black boys from CORE see this car, well, they're gonna think we're the Bureau and they're gonna get real upset.'

'Why do I need to register anyway?'

'Christ, we went over that!' Banister took a long, deep drag of his cigar. 'We need a reason to be there. Don't you see? We just can't park there, because they'll figure we're the Bureau just trying to spook them. Now, we'll be there in a couple of minutes, so take this in.'

Oswald leant forward and listened intently to Banister. The aroma from the cigar lingered in the car making Lee's eyes itchy. Banister didn't take his eyes off Oswald.

The black Cadillac moved slowly down the gritty, dusty road on St Helena Street, Clinton, Louisiana. They were the only vehicle moving on the road. The first vehicles they saw were Police patrol cars. One of them had its emergency lights flashing, almost lost in the gloriously sunny day.

... not a cloud in the sky ...

Lee glanced up from the rear of the car.

Several hundred colored people were walking north toward an impressive brick building at the end of the street, white policemen accompanying the crowd, batons drawn at the ready. The blacks were quiet and dignified as they ambled toward the Registrar's Office.

A certain tension could be felt, swirling through the air, through doors and windows and into the car itself. The people ahead were all, it seemed, dressed the same. No fancy clothes for them, all the men and boys wore either faded, torn and dust covered jeans or pants, with the odd yellow or brown shirt amid all the white ones.

The women, still elegant, with frilly dresses, old and worn, a little more colorful.

Oswald was witnessing this squalor for the first time. Peering over the shoulders of his colleagues, eyes popping and mouth wide open in disbelief.

'Will you look at these niggers,' spat Banister. 'Ain't they got nothin' better to do?'

Ferrie laughed as he honked the horn of his car. The blacks parted as he slowly drove through them.

Lee sat back in his seat, peering through the window on his left side, meeting the hateful gaze of the Negroes; men, women and children alike. Lee had never felt such a feeling before, even after all his travels, never seen such emotion in a pair of eyes. He felt ashamed to be there, as if he was somehow responsible for their plight.

He recalled watching Luther King on TV back in August. Such a stirring speech, so many people, black and white, yellow and red. Doctor King's oration had actually lifted Lee, sent tingles down his spine and a flood of hope through his soul. Of course, words were one thing, but actions …

As he saw it, Kennedy was the only person in the free world who could match Doctor King's charisma and charm and the only person who might get something done about the racial issue. But, he conjectured, Kennedy was only sounding like he was doing something. When it came to the crunch, JFK was probably like any other politician. After all, to get that far in Government, one had to be tough. And that was an understatement.

Lee doubted JFK would get re-elected in sixty-four. Nixon would be back and–

'Hey,' snapped Banister, 'are you in there?'

Oswald looked away from the window at Banister, 'Uh, yeah, I was just thinking.'

'I can see that. Look, we're almost there now. Remember what I told you.'

'Yes,' said Lee. 'I remember.'

The car passed Delphine Street, just a block away from the Registrar's Office, the flow of the townsfolk causing Ferrie to come to a halt for several seconds.

Ferrie cursed the crowd as the odd trio slowly advanced down the street. Oswald noticed Ferrie and Banister eyeing the crowd with a hate that was totally alien to him. Obviously, Lee knew as well as anyone from the Deep South about the loathsome feelings shared by black and white folk alike, but this kind of intensity he had somehow missed. He'd not known many blacks during his youth, so maybe that was the reason.

Lee didn't exactly love the Negroes, but neither did he hate them. He began to feel uncomfortable amongst the many hundreds of the Clinton populace, felt like a charlatan invading someone else's space and life.

Indeed, he was.

A police sergeant began to show a special interest in the black Cadillac as it cruised down Main. The sergeant stopped on the East Side of the sidewalk and studied them. Pulling a pencil and pad from his shirt breast pocket, he began writing.

'Looks like we're gonna get a ticket,' said Ferrie quietly.

Banister was unconcerned. 'He'll get more than a ticket when I'm through with him.'

Ferrie laughed at the threat, even though he knew Banister was quite serious.

'Okay, Dave. This will do.'

Banister looked out of the front windshield. He couldn't see much except the mass of the township flowing almost like water, effortless and never ending, alongside and then in front of their vehicle.

'Damn,' he muttered, moving his gray head from side to side in an effort to see through the throng of humanity peering back at him as they walked to the Registrar's Office.

'You want I should get in line yet?' enquired Oswald, impatiently.

'Wait a while. I can't see the main doors... dammit nigger, get out of the way!'

Banister half shouted at a young boy who had let go of his mother's hand and stopped directly in front of Banister's gaze. The boy must have been all of ten years old. Oswald watched him over Ferrie's shoulder.

Ferrie was occupied to his immediate left, trying to locate the police sergeant while Banister had opened the glove compartment and was flicking rapidly through some papers.

The boy smiled and his entire face lit up. Gleaming white teeth and large brown and white eyes filled his innocent young face.

Oswald returned the smile and waved, but as he did so Banister looked up and forward and saw the boy.

'Get the hell outta here,' he yelled. 'Get off the car!'

The boy lost his smile and stepped back from the vehicle, eyes opened even wider than before, a look of bewilderment smeared across his smooth young features.

Oswald was just as startled at Banister's outburst, but said nothing. The boy's mother returned, scolding her son and sending daggers of hate at the occupants of the Cadillac. Soon, she and the boy were swallowed up by the crowd.

Oswald opened the door of the car and got out. Even though it couldn't be much later than ten a.m., the sudden rush of heat almost took his breath away. The air around him was filled with the dust from the hundreds of feet scurrying toward the Registry building. Lee stood up, people filing past him, glancing at him, worried by his presence and the car's.

As he closed the door, Lee bent and said, 'See you later.'

He heard no reply and, after straightening his shirt, moved into the crowd. As he joined them for the short walk, he suddenly became aware that he was walking in his own small space. All the Negroes moved away from Lee, as if he had some deadly disease.

Of course, he had.

White skin.

Lee looked straight-ahead and avoided eye contact with anybody whilst moving with the crowd toward the building. He observed two policemen atop the steps at the entrance to the building armed with pump action shot-guns.

... mean looking bastards ... no arguing with them ...

Oswald looked away as one of the officers saw him.

... sonofabitch! I bet he can't believe his eyes ...

One Negro joined Oswald, saying, 'What you doing here, man? You ain't from around here ...'

Lee ignored the man, but he wouldn't let it go. Oswald brushed the man's hand from his shirt.

'You from the man?' he said, working himself slowly into a subdued frenzy. 'Hey, man, I'm talkin' to you!'

Oswald moved away. Other people began to mutter insults. One of the Police Officers standing on the steps had noticed the altercation and watched intently. The Negro caught on and he, too, moved away.

Oswald felt the sweat roll down his back and wiped his brow.

... no wonder there's so much trouble down here. Who can survive in this damned heat ...

Suddenly, the multitude came to a halt. A baby wailed somewhere in the crowd and Oswald remembered.

... Junie ... what would Marina think if she could see me now ... and Ruth ... she'd be at me the first opportunity she could get ...

Oswald checked for his billfold and pulled it from his pants back pocket. Opening it, he saw the two twenty dollar bills Ferrie had given him and his forged United States Navy Identification card. It bore his photo and name, but the New Orleans address was a fake. Looking up toward the large oak doors of the building, Lee could hear the rising voices in the crowd. He wasn't sure if he was causing the problem, but he couldn't dismiss it either.

Then Lee found himself at the bottom of the steps.

*

'No deal, he wouldn't do it.'

Lee settled back into the rear seat of the Cadillac and slammed the door. 'He just said I'd not been in town long enough to register. I told him about the job I was after and he said he'd heard there were no jobs left at the Hospital anyway,' Oswald shrugged and sank further into his seat.

'Did you pick up anything else?' asked Banister.

'Yes. The local CORE representative was hovering around me. I'm pretty sure he got my name. I'm also pretty sure he figured I was with the Bureau, just spooking them or whatever, like you said. Kept seeing this guy out of the corner of my eye. Everywhere I turned, he seemed to be there, just out of my vision.'

'Did you get his name?'

'Yep, Collins. Corrie Collins,' Oswald leant forward and folded his arms on the seats in front and dropped his chin onto them.

... what wouldn't I do for a cool beer now ...

'Collins,' said Banister, frowning. 'I think we've got something on him back at the office.'

... that should be interesting ... I'll have to take a look at that filing cabinet again ...

'Yes. I remember him,' interjected Ferrie, scratching the end of his nose. Lee looked at Ferrie's head.

Jesus, will you look at that wig!

'I think we ran across him in Jackson a while back,' Ferrie began to chew on the knuckle of his left thumb.

Banister looked at Ferrie and nodded. 'That's him. Sonofabitch was on a walk with King.'

Oswald's eyes flicked between the two men. Their hate for the blacks was as strong as the hate he'd felt directed at him outside in the line. He was astounded that anybody could spend the time and energy fuelling all the hate and distrust currently in the air in Clinton, Louisiana in particular and the Southern United States as a whole. But Lee knew that was a naive thought.

'How long was I out there?' asked Oswald. 'It seemed like forever.'

'It was forever,' answered Banister. 'We thought we were gonna have to come and get you out.'

'Three hours,' said Ferrie turning to Oswald. 'What was it like in there, Lee?'

'Terrible. I felt like a leper,' he laughed. 'Sure did upset them though. I thought one guy was going to kill me! I've never seen so many black people in one place. Guess they weren't keen on seeing a white guy amongst them either.'

Oswald got no response from his colleagues and was quiet.

'Well,' he said. 'What do we do now? What about finding somewhere we can eat?'

'What we do now,' replied Banister, sternly, 'is head for home.'

*

'This is Lee,' Oswald, receiver in hand, stood in the corridor against the wall holding the payphone. Around him stood the Chief and another uniform, apparently not listening to the conversation.

'Well, hi,' Ruth Paine said, quietly, on the other end of the phone line.

'Hi, uh, is Marina there?' Lee enquired, uncomfortably, 'I'd like to talk with her, please,' Oswald gazed down at the floor, the activity in the corridor distracting his attention.

'Well, no, Lee, she isn't,' Ruth replied, coldly. 'The Secret Service and FBI have taken her someplace for questioning.'

Oswald frowned and thought for a millisecond. 'Did they say where and for how long they, uh, she might be gone?' he said, desperately.

'I'm sorry, Lee, they didn't tell me anything … I'm sorry,' Ruth was now sincere, he could tell that. 'Is there anything else I could do, you know–'

'Yeah, yes, that's why I'm calling,' he interrupted, 'would you try to reach a guy for me? He's an attorney.'

'Well, sure, if I can. Where is he?' Oswald imagined his wife's friend picking up the pencil next to the pad he knew she kept by the phone.

'New York. I'll pay for the call just as soon as I get out of this mess, Ruth,' Oswald promised.

'Oh, I know you will. Don't concern yourself with that,' Ruth paused, then said, 'Are you okay?'

'Yes, as far as that goes, yeah. The guy's name is Abt, that's A …B …T. You'll find his number in the address book in the top drawer of our bedside cabinet. John Abt.'

'…Okay, I've got that …Abt.'

'Yes,' Lee looked up at Curry, who was unsmiling, sad even,

as he looked up and down the corridor. Lee gazed at the Chief until he looked back at him, then Lee turned away.

'Just what is this all about, Lee?' said Ruth, sharply.

Oswald was niggled, the way only Ruth could niggle him. 'Well, forgive me, Ruth, but I'm damn sure you know what this is all about by now–'

'I didn't mean it like that–'

Oswald held his head with his free hand.

... Jeez, the last thing I need right now is an argument with the only person on earth who can help me ...

Oswald retreated. 'My mistake,' he said, regretting his attack. 'I'm sorry. I'm just worried about Marina, that's all. Where are the kids?'

'They're okay, they're staying here tonight. I don't know how long Marina will be. We figured it best that they stay here for the meanwhile.'

... at least she's good with the girls ...

'Thanks. Have you seen my mother?'

Ruth took a second to answer, as if she had been distracted. 'Yeah, she came by with Robert earlier. She's gone now, though.'

Both had said all they had to say and a pause set in the conversation. Curry looked at Oswald, nodding his head.

'Ruth, I have to go now. Don't forget, please don't forget to make that call ... Abt, that's the guy's name.'

'Okay, I'll do it now.'

'Thanks, Ruth.'

'...yeah...'

The phone went dead and as Oswald looked into the mouth piece before replacing it, he couldn't help wondering if that had been his last contact with the outside world, that he was in way over his head. As he was led back to his lonely cell, he thought of the people he'd met that summer.

... had they gotten away, while I'm stuck in this place.

*

'Do you want to tell me where and how you lived when you got back from the Soviet Union?' Captain Fritz shuffled his papers, seemingly bored by the continuation of the interrogation.

'That's easy,' said Lee, 'I lived just about everywhere and didn't eat too well.'

Fritz sighed, looking at Lee over his glasses. 'Can you give us some details ...'

Oswald straightened his back and sat up in the chair.

...now Captain, these are the kind of questions that I like... I can go on all day with this kind of stuff...

'Well, I lived with my brother for a while in Fort Worth. After some interference from my mother, Marina and I moved to Dallas. We stayed on, uh, Mercedes Street, I think it was ... uh, it's been a while, anyway, it wasn't the greatest of places in the world, but it was all I could afford at the time. The FBI began pestering me and my wife at around this time. They never get out of your hair. Anyway–'

'What did they talk to you about? In connection with what?' Hosty questioned.

...you know what, Hosty! You were the one who pestered us... but, I'll play your game as long as you like...

'they asked me what I did in the Soviet Union.'

'And what was that?'

'Like did I work for the Russians, was I contacted by the Soviet Secret Police and the like. I told them that I made no deals with representatives of that Intelligence Community and that I was not a Soviet agent or anything like that. Of course, if I told you that I wasn't approached by these people, you'd know I was lying. They did approach me and I did talk with them. I didn't have much choice in that, I should add at this point, the situation being what it was at the time.'

'And what was the situation?'

'Well, they were about to throw me out of the country. They gave me a couple of weeks to sort myself out. I told them I wanted to stay, but they weren't about to let me.'

'Get back to the FBI-' Fritz ignored Hosty's glare.

'I also told the FBI of my undesirable discharge from the Marines. They weren't too interested in that area, just didn't give a damn. I told them I would not discuss with them why I went to Russia. They never leave you alone. They told me they wanted to talk to my wife and I said for them to forget it. But they did anyway, when I wasn't there.'

'How many times did they speak with you, since you came back?'

'Two or three times, I don't know. As soon as they were gone, I'd get them out of my head.'

'We have information that you and your family stayed with some prominent Russian speaking members of the community. Tell us about that.' Agent Hosty finally got back into the questioning.

'My wife and I became acquainted and quite friendly with the steadily growing number of those people in the Dallas area. These were people from the European theater, tied together with common interests, such as country of origin, religion and, of course, language.'

'Were these people of Russian origin?'

'If you mean were they all Reds, I'd say no. They were people from the Eastern European block countries. Stalin's so called buffer states. My wife gave conversational Russian lessons to one family we met.'

'And who were they? What were their names?'

'Uh, let me think... yeah, they were called Gregory.'

'And what was Mister Gregory's line of business?'

'Petrochemicals, I believe. I don't remember.'

'Go on.'

'Well, Marina was paid for the lessons. We went to their house a good deal. We got on okay with them. One of them had been born in Leningrad, the same place as my wife and he was anxious to talk with Marina.'

'This is Gregory?'

'No, some other guy. I don't remember his name.'

'Would you know a George de Mohrenschildt?'

George the laughing man from... someplace...

'Yes, I met him around the same time.'

'What relationship did you have with him, if any?'

... you'd not believe me if I told you ...

'De Mohrenschildt... none. He was there and I met him.'

... George, the man to talk to, talk with. The best conversations I had in my whole life were with George...

'Did you know he is suspected of being a Nazi spy?'

Oswald laughed. 'Well, thanks! I needed that! Don't be ridiculous. He was an engineer and a gifted artist. Nazi spy!' Oswald mocked the detective.

'How would you know if he were or not?'

'That's just ridiculous.'

'Lee, did you buy a rifle from, uh ...' Captain Fritz looked at the notes on his paper, 'Klein's Rifle Store of Chicago, Illinois?'

Little had changed for Lee. He noticed a different air about the Police Captain. The man had obviously been home, or at least had had the opportunity to shower, shave and change from his usual blue suit into a neat brown one. The Captain, who, Lee guessed, must have been in his fifties, looked refreshed and cool, totally different from the last time they had spoken.

Oswald gritted his teeth. 'I have never been to Chicago, Illinois,' he spoke softly, 'and I have never bought a rifle... didn't we cover this?'

Fritz stood, ignoring Oswald and began to move around the office, reading from his scrap of paper.

'From where did you obtain the revolver you shot Officer Tippit with? You must have bought it from somewhere...'

Lee scratched his head and shook it, saying, 'I have a complaint that I'd like putting on the record,' Oswald paused, the policemen in attendance all looked at him. 'I want to complain that I wasn't allowed to wear a similar jacket in that so-called line-up I was in before. I informed the policeman there that it would prejudice the outcome of any identification the witness or witnesses you had behind the screen. None of them looked like me, didn't even look remotely like me. I really must protest about my treatment during my, uh, stay here. I–'

Fritz interrupted. 'Lee, let's not get into any long, drawn out speeches again. We have a great deal to go over and-'

'I am not a malcontent,' Oswald interrupted, 'I have views about this situation, of course I do. But I cannot speak freely because I don't have legal representation, and,' Oswald slammed his fist down on the desk again, 'you people are stopping me getting through to anyone!'

'What are you hiding, Lee?' said Fritz, slowly and coldly, looking deeply into Oswald's eyes. 'Why do I get the feeling that you know a lot more about this than you're saying? Why don't you make some kind of statement? Instead of complaining all the time, why don't you just come right out and say it?'

Oswald stared back at the Captain. Fritz was, of course, right in that instance.

...I do have a lot to say on the situation, my friend, stuff that would knock your socks off...

10

Lee Oswald looked out over the balcony of his fifth floor hotel room, the hustle and bustle of Mexico City flowing below him in the glaring, dry, noontime sun. A long depression had set on him again and he felt like nothing more than a spare part, lost in a strange place, waiting, endlessly waiting.

Lee was deep in thought, wistfully gazing down into the suburbs through glazed eyes.

Three days ... three long days, sat in this place, talking to no-one, seeing no-one ... a boring bus journey, shaking my weary bones until they almost shattered ... that stupid Mex border guard, with nothing better to do than hold the whole Goddamn world up while he checks suitcases and baggage. Money ... it's all to do with money ... the sonofabitch wanted some money to stop his crazy antics ... four thousand dollars, locked away in the bus station in New Orleans ... and I'm here, without a beer, without a decent change of clothes, plumbing doesn't work when I need it, no shower since the day I got here.

Lee could smell a certain sweetness in the air around him, hoped it wasn't him, that it was how Mexico City would normally smell on an autumn day.

Serious ... the situation is so serious. Hanging around with lunatics for the past six months ... and now all those same lunatics are walking around this place, this hot, dry, shit hole of a place, planning in little rooms with no air conditioning, planning to shoot the President, commit a crime like that.

Lee thought of Banister, that crazy alcoholic, his boss for the past summer.

Where would he be now? Probably back in New Orleans, working out of Camp Street, with even more Cubans running errands for him, for a few dollars, passing out leaflets on street corners, being filmed by the FBI, John Edgar saving their fleeting images for posterity on grainy, black and white Government Issue celluloid ... never being shown to the public. Have to get away from this somehow, someway ... soon ... serious stuff ...

Oswald looked at his finger, the finger he'd taken a slice off the day after his arrival in Mexico City.

Damn nail, why didn't someone fix it ... it was sore, but I'll kept the wound clean... damn place... no Band-Aids, no nothing ...

DelGado didn't like Mexico either...

A fling in Tihuana, years ago, had only resulted in illness from the tequila and penicillin shots because of the women. Lee laughed at the thought of his Marine buddies chasing women around town, spending all their pay on them, chatting to them, listening to them giggling because they knew as much English as you knew Spanish.

... but DelGado was Hispanic, could speak Spanish real well ... but I knew Russian ...

Oswald rested his chin on his hands clasping the rail. Turning his thoughts to his other 'contact', he'd long presumed that he couldn't be the only informer to penetrate the group, that there must be at least one other. He had no way of knowing who that might be and, he reasoned, they probably wouldn't know who he was either.

The cars and people flowed under him, coming from nowhere, going nowhere. But they were on the streets, free to roam wherever they wished.

Trapped, in this place - what are they all doing down there, why did Ferrie tell me not to leave the hotel room for any reason ... food left outside on a tray ... and why has he not been to see me ... no phone call, message or visit ... maybe he's dead, ha, or gone back to New Orleans! Music, no music.

... George ... De Mohrenschildt ... son of a ... noble man, exile from Czarist Russia ... escaped to Poland with family during Russian Revolution, nineteen-seventeen ... my contact in Dallas area ... fluent in five languages, Russian, Spanish, Polish, German, French ... what was he doing now, in Haiti ... what does he do ... geologist ...petro chemicals, that kind of thing ... what connections did he have to Yugoslavia ... father jailed before reaching Poland ... the last time I saw him, just before I went to New Orleans ... Guatemala, he was in Guatemala in sixty-one, for the Bay of Pigs ... Ferrie, Guatemala in sixty-one for the Bay of Pigs ... surely scum like Ferrie couldn't be involved with George? Could he? George's idea for me to go to New Orleans. Banister, Dave Ferrie ...

New Orleans …

How does a rich, successful man in Dallas get mixed up with that New Orleans crowd? Just the same way as a rich successful man in the White House does … it's the times … how does a poor, unsuccessful man get to be stuck in a hot, sticky rundown apartment on the seedy side of downtown Mexico City … by meeting a rich, successful man in Dallas who sends him off to meet some low life cronies, who just happen to be, one way or another, mixed up in the same business as he is.

Oswald wiped his brow and pulled his sticky shirt away from his uncomfortable chest.

Shower, why don't they fix the blasted shower …

Lee moved back into the apartment, to the phone.

No outside calls, remember, no-one must know that you're here … no-one cares where the hell I am, much less here …

As Lee reached the black phone, putting his hand upon the receiver, he paused.

No-one to know I'm here … they know me as Hidell here, Alek James Hidell… all I want is what I'm paying for … a room with a shower, didn't think I needed to specify ' room with a shower that works, please' for Godsakes…

Oswald walked away from the phone, sat on the small bed and stared ahead at the wall opposite. He leant back against the thin partition behind him, which felt cool against his wet back. Bringing up his hands, he began rubbing his tired face.

Not much sleep… tired all the time … why doesn't something happen … anything.

Lee folded his arms in front of him and glanced around his room.

Can't even be bothered to read, too damn hot, not even hungry … must try and eat something worth eating tonight … to hell with it, I'm out tonight … get some decent food, someplace …

What about those Cubans are they here in Mexico? A strange crowd, a real bunch of weirdos really pissed when RFK put the fin-

ger on them at the Lake. Well, can see their point, really... but shooting at the FBI? They really must be crazy... still, they'd better go do some jobs for Banister or Ferrie. They'll need the money ... to think they'd try and get Castro out of Cuba, risking all that ... admirable, I suppose, in an off the wall way. Maybe if they spent their energies in some other way... be more successful...

Ruby with his guns and girls ... the Carousel Club in Dallas, meeting him with Clem in Baton Rouge in the summer ... Jeeps ... Ruby could lay his hands on jeeps, damnit... where the hell do you store fifty jeeps, after you've gotten hold of them? Ruby and that hat, he must sleep and bathe in that hat!

As Lee listened to the traffic in the streets outside and below, fresh feelings of frustration flooded over him.

Ferrie had already told him to return to Dallas by October the fourth, only a few days away. Oswald had the distinct impression that he wouldn't be seeing Ferrie before then, so whom was he to see here?

... probably no one ...

He brooded, the sounds of car horns and angry exchanges so far below.

...stuck here, on my own, not that that in itself is a problem, but no music or anything...

Lee pulled himself off the bed and back to the window as he realized he was heading down the same dark, dismal track as before. Wishing he could walk out of the sweltering heat of the apartment into the cooler air outside, he again became aware of the clammy condition of his clothes.

... God, send a breeze, just a slight breeze for five minutes ...

Lee's mind raced back to the end of the fifties, when he'd gotten involved with Intelligence in the Marines.

In the four years since I left for Russia, what have I achieved? Mixed up in what people would call the spy game, photographing installations near Minsk, the NKVD knowing I was doing it, giving away old military secrets to gain their confidence... failing...

What is a spy anyway? I've read all the James Bond drivel and all the other stuff years ago … ordinary people think being a spy is a glamorous life: wine, women and all the trimmings of success, just like Bond. But they're wrong, it's not like that at all … I must have been crazy going to Russia at such an early age… but how do you say 'no'? You can't. That's what I chose, that's what I wanted - that's what I got. The money? The money is in a deposit box in New Orleans and I can't even get a cold beer or even a warm one - th-ose photos of Minsk, some are still in my kit bag back at Ruth's house with my 'spy' stuff.

Lee saw himself in his mind's eye, back in Moscow, back in Minsk, looking for vapor trails over the city. He'd monitored the U2 spy planes, the CIA's *Black Lady* of espionage, dozens of times. He knew it was overhead, had signaled the pilot … but he saw no vapor trails. Since the downing of a U2 plane, six months after Lee had volunteered his Marine secrets to the Soviet Embassy staff, he couldn't help wondering if the information he had passed on had been responsible for the Soviet Airforce bringing down that plane but he had to doubt it.

It was some coincidence that the plane had been lost just as Eisenhower and Khrushchev were about to set upon peace talks, that may have led, many were hoping, to some form of thawing in the Cold War. A sobering thought was that he knew that just as many people around the world were hoping for the opposite.

The plane had come down and the moment was lost, the conference did go ahead, in a fashion, but any whisper of peace was cancelled by a rightly embittered Khrushchev.

Goddamn vapor trails … we knew there wouldn't be any, what was the problem … the only vapor trails I saw in all my time there was on May Day, during the parade … did I go to Russia for two and a half years to watch for vapor trails?

The Minsk factory job, electronics. What a joke! The parties were good though, a few 'friends' sure, they were all in on it, all watching me, NKVD, all of them, probably Marina too, but she loves me and

I love her.

Oswald chuckled as he imagined Marina's uncle's face when she told him she was dating an American defector.

An ex-Marine with radar secrets coming out of his ears. Uncle Ilya. Was he MVD or NKVD, the Soviets have as many intelligence operations and agencies as the United States. Uncle Ilya was certainly up to something, he even got out his best Brandy when he met me for the first time. Wasn't he an engineer, supposedly in the ... MVD. Yes, that's it, MVD.

Oswald recalled looking at Marina's papers before they left the Soviet Union bound for Holland.

They were faked, dammit ... fakes! But what had Marina to hide? Was Marina NKVD ... maybe she had been, maybe she trained for that line, but it didn't matter now. Of course, she had been a member of the Komsomol, the Communist Party youth movement... catch 'em while they're young. One thing always bothered me she went on 'holiday' for several months before she met me. Had she been in training for something?

Oswald's paranoia was getting the better of him.

Marina, a Soviet agent? I doubt it ... but why not? Was she 'on' to me? Surely, it makes sense, the NKVD knew I was there, I told them so but now, before I go crazy... it doesn't matter. She is in Dallas, waiting for me, with Junie and another baby on the way ... a sister for Junie would be best ... although a son would be nice ... with any luck, the new baby will be born on my birthday, the eighteenth of October - we'd be twins!

Those six long weeks, interrogated by God knows how many KGB officers... they start on you as soon as you appear, Intourist guides and interpreters, wherever you are, they're sure to follow. And me, a United States Marine, fresh from Atsugi, Japan, the U2, all of that, a prize indeed. They knew who I was, why I was there ... shipped to Minsk, out of the way, classified as Stateless ... four hundred and fifty miles from Moscow and my mission - vapor trails! Vapor trails ... but what a great apartment! The movies, a girl on my arm, more money to spend than I ever had!

The language training school near Minsk, CIA reckoned they knew about it and they were right! Those stupid commies, taught me how to eat, speak and shit the Russian language, all for free. Two way mirrors, top security, guards with dogs and machine guns, a high concrete wall, barbed wire...

The heat haze of downtown Mexico City shimmered over the landscape, obscuring the pretty hills to the north.

... be nice and cool up in those mountains, better for the lungs than this place ... almost like Los Angeles, Mexico City ... stifling, too many people hanging around on corners, waiting to rob you, New York and all that ... New York ...

... no place in Russia like New York, and no place over there like New Orleans ... such a melting pot, New Orleans ...

Lee exhaled, sadly. His mind back in New Orleans, his boredom surrounding him, enveloping him, suffocating him. As he looked at his injured finger again, it began to throb. Putting it to his mouth, Oswald licked the cut for the millionth time.

My job at the NASA installation, what's happened to that... Bishop must have some information on that by now... maybe it's waiting for me back in Dallas... hope so... then back to New Orleans, for good this time, with Marina and the kids, working at the Space Facility ... better work, better money ... a chance to spend some of that cash holed up in the bus station.

Oswald dropped his head onto his hands as they again held the rail surrounding the balcony, the flaking, rusty paint reminding him of Ferrie's run down apartment.

Sighing deeply, Oswald's weariness began to drown him. His thoughts moved to Miami and Dallas and the possibility of an attempt on the President's life. Although he'd not been privvy to any discussions for the proposed Miami hit, Lee knew the attempt would bear the same hallmarks as the Dallas 'back-up'. He silently hoped the Miami attack would be the one to see fruition, knowing he'd be out of any immediate danger should that be the case.

Dallas, of course, was different. By this point, he had been leaving information in his 'dead-drop' in downtown New Orleans, picked up by God-knows-who.

Must be the FBI, only they would know of it … that's what Bishop had told him …

Those months before when he first stumbled on the assassination attempt in Ferrie's apartment.

Ferrie is a fag…

Various sordid images ran through his mind. He recalled a photograph of Ferrie and some of Dave's friends he'd been shown, all clothed in drag, large smiles on their made-up faces, prancing merrily in the privacy of Ferrie's apartment.

The thought sickened Lee and he cast it from his mind.

… lunch, what can I get for lunch …

He was hungry and thirsty.

… must get out of here today …just to clear my head, stuck in here forever, in this heat …

The little cash he had with him lay on the bedside cabinet and he moved back into the apartment and again sat on the bed. Sitting down on it, Lee picked up the miserable stack of pesos and began to count.

… should have kept this in bucks … could have traded for more, had extra bargaining power … still, this'll see me through until I see Ferrie… if I get to see him … where the hell can he be … what about the jobs I'm supposed to be doing here?

… Fuck this, I'm going out …

Lee stood, thrust the money deep into his pocket and moved to the door and a measured kind of sanity beyond it.

*

Got to get away … from here, from these nuts … shoot, shoot the President, kill the President … murder … blood on the streets, shoot the … gun down the President . . . get away, run, far away … life in danger …in Moscow, Minsk everywhere I go … danger, danger all around. Too dangerous to stay around this place … take photo-

graphs of ... don'tgetcaught, NKVD ... kill ... get money to Marina ... tomorrow ... get money from post office box soon as possible ...

Lee . . .Get away ... from here ... Get out ... ... Kill them all get them all ...the children, get the children out! Marina! Marina! Get the children out!!!

Lee ...Arrest them, kill them ... the President! Shoot! Don't shoot the President! No! No!! Stop them all ...

Must be a way out from all this ... Never alone, get away from me ... Another beer? Sure ... lots where this came from! Money? Sure ... lots where this came from ... but don't go . . . stay a while . . .there's nobody about who'll see you ... can' t seem to break out ...

Mmm ...no ... no ... lots of money ... in cash if youneeditbadlyenough ... Lee! Lee!

Uh . . .

Oswald sat upright in his bed, sweat pouring from his thin frame, the bed soaking wet, beads of perspiration hanging from his eyebrows, running down his nose, cheeks, chin, neck, chest, back - trickling like a mountain stream over his shoulders, down, down onto his arms, wrists, hands and fingers.

The light from the near see-through drawn curtains covering the sliding window before him stabbed into his brain and Lee screwed up his eyes tightly.

'Lee?'

There, again, that voice invading his mind, again, again ...

'Wha ...'

Oswald felt strong hands grip his shoulders and then he was being shaken like a doll, sweat breaking free from the end of his nose and chin, falling onto his naked body.

'Lee! For God's sake, wake up!'

Oswald's eyes focused on the figure sat over him. David Ferrie's bright red hair catching the light, eyebrows ever-arched in surprise, ears hanging from the sides of his head. Ferrie's eyes pierced Oswald's, trying to see the back of Lee's head.

'Mm ...'

...Fag bastard ... heads banging ... boy, must have moved some booze last night . . .

Ferrie shook him again, slippery hands digging deeply into Lee's arms. Oswald shook his head.

'Yeah,' he said quietly, then louder, 'yeah, I'm awake...'

Ferrie let go. 'You were dreaming!' said Ferrie. 'Boy, were you having a doozy!' Ferrie laughed as Lee pulled the top sheet from under the blankets and wiped his face. Oswald held the sheet closer and exhaled loudly into it.

'What the hell was that about?' Lee said, almost in a whisper. 'Jeez, I don't need anything like that again...'

Ferrie looked at him. 'You were talking about Marina ... and money.'

'Money?' Oswald laughed. 'Yeah! I need a raise, Dave.'

Ferrie laughed again and tipped his head to one side. 'Did you get that money to her yet?'

'No,' said Oswald continuing to wipe himself on the already soiled sheet, 'I couldn't explain where I'd got that amount of cash from... she'd think I'd robbed a bank or something.'

'Just what I would have thought, too,' Ferrie stood up and moved away from the bed to the sliding door. He opened it, mixing the stale stench of Oswald's slumber with the humid air of Mexico City.

'Nagell tried that, yesterday morning ...'

'Nagell..?' Oswald stood and moved into the bathroom, keeping the sheet around him. 'Who's Nagell?' he shouted, turning on the cold tap.

Ferrie looked out over the city.

'Agency,' he answered. 'Must have gone crazy. Walked into the First National Bank in El Paso and tried to rob the place. Got arrested, then the local Feds dragged him away for questioning.'

'Nagell ... never heard of the guy,' Oswald shouted from

the bathroom.

'Just as well … he's been tailing you ever since you came back from Moscow.'

Ferrie turned and looked at the bathroom door as he heard the tap stop running abruptly. Oswald appeared, dressed now in his underpants, mouth full of toothpaste, eyes wide, ashen faced.

'That's right,' continued Ferrie. 'The guy's been tailing you for almost a year and a half. We think he was turned around, working for the KGB as well as the Agency. Banister came across him in New Orleans, you know, he was asking questions and stuff.'

'What the hell did Banister do?' Oswald spat through the toothpaste.

'We watched him. Kept tabs on him for a while, but we lost him later on in the summer. He knew you from Atsugi, don't you remember him?'

Oswald shook his head, looking down at the floor.

'Looks like he was tailing you for the KGB. Why, we're not sure. Banister thought it may have been something to do with your work last year on the Cuban missile photographs. He'd been tagging you and was about to move in on you while you were working at the lab… anyway, the Feds have him now, so don't worry about it.'

Oswald moved back into the bathroom.

… followed … by this guy … for the Soviets … why didn't Bishop or Banister warn me … Nagell, don't remember that name … four years is a long time … met lots of guys in the service …

Ferrie appeared at the bathroom doorway, Oswald looked up to see him reflected in the mirror. Lee continued to brush his teeth as Ferrie spoke.

'Lee,' he said, 'we think he was going to kill you.'

Oswald looked up sharply and stared at Ferrie. 'Kill–'

'That's only what we think. We don't know and guess we'll never know now. The Feds have him, and that's about the size of it,' Ferrie paused, Oswald turned on the tap again and splashed his face with cold water over and over.

... how much more of this ... how much . . .

'Hey,' said Ferrie, moving behind Oswald. Ferrie put his hand on Lee's back. Oswald stood up, bolt upright, his head slowly starting to ache again.

'It's okay,' continued Ferrie, as Oswald moved away from him and pulled a towel from the rail next to the bath tub, 'he's out of the way now. Don't worry about it.' Ferrie smiled.

'Yeah,' answered Oswald, bringing the off-white towel to his face, rubbing it and his head vigorously. 'So I will worry about it. Why the hell did you bother to tell me, if this guy is out of the way?'

Ferrie recoiled as if injured, his mouth dropping open slightly.

'Why tell me now, huh? You didn't tell me three months ago, while the guy was stalking me! Now you tell me, he's gotten arrested by the Feds, out of the picture ... and now you tell me to forget about it!'

'Lee, I–'

'Keep it, Dave,' Oswald threw down the towel and pushed past Ferrie. 'That kind of shit I don't need right now.'

Lee pulled on his trousers and socks. Reaching under the bed, he pulled out his shoes. After donning them, he bent over to tie up the laces, his head began to spin with the sudden revelation and the alcohol from the night before. 'Anybody else out there I should worry about, huh?' He said, bitterly. Lee dropped a lace.

... damn ...

Ferrie joined him on the bed, sitting next to him.

'Well, the only answer to that is yourself,' Oswald looked at Ferrie as he continued. 'My guess is that you're an idiot. Judging by the state you're in now and the fact that I smell booze on you ... we heard you were out last night.'

Lee blushed. 'Only in the bar across the street ... I–'

'Keep it. You were told not to go out, Lee. Luckily for you, one of our Cuban friends had the foresight to keep tabs on you. Boy, you were gone - totally out of your head!'

Oswald held his head. 'Don't I know it …'

Ferrie stood, thrusting his hands into the pockets of his olive green fatigues, 'Listen, we all have to let our hair down, I know. But orders is orders.'

Lee held his hands up. 'Yeah, I'm sorry …'

'We got work to do today, Lee,' Ferrie said, ignoring Oswald's apology. 'We gotta meet some people. Later on this evening. First, you'll need some money. You spent quite a lot last night and owe the bar more than you spent.'

Oswald looked sheepish.

'Don't worry. It's been taken care of. Do you remember coming back up here last night?'

'…no…'

Oswald wiped under his arms and silently cursed the useless shower and Ferrie at the same time, not knowing which he'd like to kick the most.

'Here', Ferrie tossed a wad of US Dollars onto the bed. Oswald put down the towel and picked up the money.

'There's three hundred for you. I told Clem you'd been a good boy, not asked any questions and had done as you were told these past three or four days. Forget about last night. Now, finish dressing, get a shave, there's a nice little barber three blocks over. Get out there and then get something decent to eat. You might want to get Marina a present, or maybe the kid, I don't know.'

Ferrie sighed and straightened his shirt.

Oswald's eyes followed him as the elder man walked to the door.

'Just one thing,' Ferrie said turning on his heel, raising a pointed finger at Lee. 'Be down stairs in the bar outside by six tonight. Do what you want today, but be there.'

Ferrie closed the door behind him and was gone.

11

Oswald felt his face for the fiftieth time that evening. The shave Ferrie had recommended had been the closest of his short life. Lee felt no stubble, as was usually the case only a few hours after he shaved himself. Smoke was already filling the small room, beginning to choke him, leaving him irritable and uncomfortable.

Not a time to get uptight about cigarette smoke … this place … CIA safe house? … looks neat … could just be someone's pad … but doesn't have that… lived in feel …

Lee picked up a can of beer and opened it. The hiss of the ringpull was followed by a steady stream of Coors spilling out over his hand.

Shit … trust me to get the one that's shook up … damn...

Oswald wiped his hand and looked about the room as he did so. Two Cubans in the corner were chattering away in Spanish, smoking something a little stronger than a cigarette, they were getting louder and louder, as they talked and laughed incessantly. Lee did not recognize either of them.

Ferrie was stood at the drinks cabinet, talking to Billy. As Oswald watched, Billy would occasionally glance over at Oswald and then look away.

… Billy's looking very neat tonight … nice crisp shirt and jacket … sipping his beer, not throwing it back like the last time I saw him … looks pretty smart tonight …

Ferrie's conversation gently fell onto Oswald's ears. He sat on the sofa, mesmerized by Ferrie's monologue. Ferrie talked softly to the young American, pulling him deeper and deeper into his web.

… where have I heard all that before …

' …so, back in the late fifties, Bobby Kennedy was just about making a name for himself, but that was all. On the McClellan Committee he became a little bit of a nuisance, but nothing more. You know the type, eager, young, rich kid Attorney-at-Law trying to get some power, you know, impress his dad, that kind of thing.'

Ferrie took a sip of his drink and gazed into Billy's eyes. 'The guy has a million dollars, wakes up one morning and thinks, "what the hell can I do today? Screw a couple of women? Go out with the guys? Nah, I know, I'll go get Al Capone", you know, that kind of thing.'

Billy's smile extended right across his face, showing crooked teeth.

'Anyhow, when he campaigns for his big brother and gets the sonofabitch elected to President, the guy who got him there wants his piece, and why not? So, his brother says, "why don't you be head of the CIA?" The wimp, not knowing that he could do a lot better covering his brother's back by doing just that, says, "nah, let me sort out that fag Hoover!"'

Billy laughed, deeply. Ferrie continued, animated by now, revelling in the attention.

'So when ol' Jack beats Dicky out of sight, you know, by a rigged vote arranged by his dad, or so the story goes, he says to his little brother "You know, I never realized that you were so good at anything, except maybe screwing the broads, so, hey! Why not be Attorney General and sort out that fag Hoover?", And Bobby says, "Yeah! Why didn't I think of that?" and Jack says, "that's why I'm President, Bob!"'

'Just like that, huh!' said Billy, drinking even more beer, leaning onto the wall, standing in front of the drinks cabinet.

Ferrie smiled, his stuck on eyebrows moving up his forehead amid the wrinkles.

'Just like that, yeah!' Ferrie scratched his head. 'And that pimp Lawford, the English guy. What an actor! So many great movies from him! If anybody ever landed on his feet, it's Lawford. He's even less talented than the Attorney General!'

Billy bent forward at the waist, trying to contain his laughter.

Oswald watched them, transfixed, not speaking to anybody. He turned to look at the two Cubans sat against the wall to his left. Still smoking something, they babbled on to each other, the odd belch interrupting the fluidity and beauty of the Latin language.

Lee gulped at his beer.

... and where might Clem be? ... and how many more are going to come to this little party ...

As this thought shot through Lee's mind, a loud knock came on the door. Lee heard Ferrie make his excuses to a wide-eyed Billy, put down his drink and go to answer the call.

Oswald turned and looked at Billy, who was by now on his way over to Lee with two cans of beer.

'Here,' said Billy, reaching him. 'You want a refill?'

'Sure, thanks,' Lee took the beer and opened it.

Billy sat on the sofa next to him and took a loud gulp from his beer and wiped his mouth.

'That guy is crazy!'

'I'll drink to that,' said Lee, watching Ferrie disappear into the hallway.

'We've met before, right?' inquired Billy.

... saw you training at Lake Pontchartrain with the other Cubans ... Ferrie told me you were an excellent shot ...

Oswald looked at him. 'Yeah, in Dave's apartment in New Orleans. I think you'd just had a run in with the Feds.'

'Yeah,' Billy's eyes glazed over. 'Lost two of the guys that day ... two of the best.'

'Yeah, that's too bad,' lied Oswald. 'Heard it was rough.'

Billy gulped more beer, then said, 'Not as rough as the Bay of Pigs.'

Oswald's eyes widened. 'Bay of Pigs? You were there?'

... Agency ... nah, just an adventurer . . .

'Yep, sure was. Spent over three hours in the water.

Originally I was in the first strike, but got relegated to the backup. Saved my life,' Billy looked downcast, Lee could almost hear the sounds of battle, the smell of the sea, the smell of the terror.

Billy rested his head on the back of the sofa. 'Sat in a small boat with nine other guys watching the fireworks on the beach. Airplanes were s'posed to come and strafe the jungle area, north of the beach, clear any of Fidel's men out of that area. Never came. Lot of good men fell and didn't get up again.'

Billy crushed the beer can in his right hand. 'So, JFK let us down. Didn't send in the 'planes.'

'That's too bad,' said Oswald, hoping he wasn't sounding as patronizing as he thought he was.

'Say,' he continued, nodding his head at the can, changing the subject, 'I kinda thought you were a drinker.'

Billy laughed. 'Well, maybe I am,' he sat back further into the gray sofa, 'but tonight I aim to keep a clear head. We got company, make no mistake.'

Oswald looked over at the door, a group of people were walking into the room.

… a woman … two more Cubans . . .Clem … and … Jack Ruby. … you sonofabitch, Ruby … wonder if he sold those jeeps yet … the woman … what the hell is a woman doing in this …

Ferrie appeared with another white male, dressed in a dark suit, his arm around him, both laughing.

'… so I say to the guy "get the hell outta here!"' Ferrie laughed as he spoke and the other man slapped him on the back.

Ruby and Clem crossed the room and sat on the dining chairs in front of the television set, to Oswald's right. Both were dressed in suits, but Clem had dispensed of his usual white shirt for a more casual top. One of the original fatigue-clad Cubans stood and gave his chair to the woman, dressed in slacks and blouse.

… blond hair … green eyes … about thirty-five, nice figure … Agency or girlfriend …

'Okay,' began Ferrie, 'we need to move on this, so I'll come straight to the point. Most of you know each other in some capacity. Those of you who don't, don't worry about it,' Ferrie scratched his head as if lost for words, then regained his composure.

'Uh, if you want a drink, then help yourself. There's whisky and beer, might be some gin or something in there too. Just get what you want. Sandwiches are in the kitchen, but we'll save those for later, if that's okay with everyone …'

Nobody spoke. Ferrie continued by opening the whisky bottle and pouring a large glass for himself. 'Okay, Clem's gonna take over from here … Clem?'

All eyes moved to Clem, his six foot-six, one-eighty pound frame got up from his chair and carried on rising. A shock of white-gray, tightly curled hair sat on top of his head as he moved over to the drinks cabinet. Pouring a glass of whisky for himself, Clem shot a glance at Ruby. Ruby nodded and Clem filled another, picked up both glasses and moved back to his chair.

Still nobody spoke. Clem was in command.

'Okay, let's see what we've got,' he said, his voice surprisingly low for such a big man. Clem passed Ruby his whisky.

'We're working on a three pronged movement. That is to say, the President is coming down to Miami in late November, around the twentieth. The day after that visit, the Presidential party moves onto Fort Worth and then Dallas.'

… Dallas … Marina …

'We can't get to him in Fort Worth, our contacts say the security at the airfield will be too tight, so we're not even thinking about there.' Clem took a sip of his drink. 'We got two places lined up in Dallas. First of all, some place in downtown and then the Trade Mart. Kennedy is giving a lunch time speech there around one o'clock.'

Clem looked at all of them in turn.

'Best place is Miami. That's where the biggest movement will be. I've got people trying to get more details as we speak.'

Billy spoke, sharply and to the point. 'Who's doing the hit there?'

Clem looked at him. 'We've got some Cubans for Miami. It's their hit. I've got a separate unit in there already. None of you know any of them. That's the way they wanted it and it sounded good to me. Anybody got any complaints on that?'

Everybody looked around for one dissenting voice. There were none.

Ruby just stared at the floor, holding his fedora in his right hand.

Oswald looked over at him.

As Ruby chewed at his lower lip, apparently nervous about the meeting or maybe something unrelated, he seemed distant, disinterested in the conversation. Oswald watched as Ruby looked deeply into his glass, his circular hand movement causing waves of whisky to smash against the sides of the tumbler. Ruby's long nose betrayed his Jewish background and his heavy double chin rested snugly on his shirt top. Hair receding, swept back over his bald patch, Ruby looked a sad and forlorn figure sat amongst these men talking murder. Ruby sat there, stone-faced, gloom pouring out of every pore.

... where the hell does Ruby come into this? Thought he was just small time ... a long ways away from his club in Dallas ... a mob connection ...

'Okay. Don't feel too bad if you're not involved in the final job. You'll all be getting good bonuses anyhow. It'll be sweeter if you don't have to do anything for it.'

... looks like I'll going back to Dallas soon ...

'So, I take it we're for the Dallas job?' Lee took the bull by the horns.

'Yes,' said Ferrie. 'Though I can assure you, Lee you won't be doing any shooting!' Ferrie laughed, Clem and Ruby joined in.

... damn straight, you fag assed lunatic ... go on, have your fun ... I'll see you behind bars ...

'The decision has been made, let there be no mistake about that. We are still working out some kind of camouflage, some kind of fallback. We will need a scapegoat, some 'madman' to pin the blame on. Now, as I said, we're still working on that.'

The woman spoke for the first time, quietly. 'What if the scapegoat gets away, or is found not guilty?'

'By that time we would hope to be far enough away not to be implicated. It doesn't really matter if he is found innocent, probably will be. Somebody would be picked up by the police anyway, just to throw the public off.

'The police would do it, not just to set someone up, but just to get some breathing space. This 'nut' would, of course, act like a magnet for the public wrath, taking the blame, absorbing any tricky situations or questions for a good while, serving as our cover while we disappear.'

Clem smiled. 'The interesting thing is that it's not actually a federal crime to kill the President.'

'What do you mean by that?' said the girl.

'What I mean by that is just that. The FBI would find the case out of their jurisdiction as a matter of law. They would not be able to conduct the investigation. The local authorities would be obliged to do so. We have people stalking the President all the time. They're not gonna kill him, they're just there to keep him in our sights, that way we can learn how the Secret Service go about their business, what they do, what they don't do. What we do know about the Secret Service of this administration is this,' Clem looked at Ferrie. ' On the whole, they are used in a variety of ways, all unrelated to their specific work, which is, of course, the protection of the President. They have been known to give out souvenirs and so on to the crowds. They don't appear to have any form of leadership.'

'Now, I don't know about that for sure, so I'll assume they do. But it's an odd thing, when you get down to it ... anyhow, that's not our problem. One thing I can be specific on is this. Their average age at present is forty and they only train officially on the shooting range twice a year. That's ridiculous. Their reflexes are never tested, but why should they be? They don't go around shooting anyhow, it's not their line. They are there to anticipate such an occurrence, to put themselves in the line of fire, as it were. The Secret Service are totally dependent on the local police for information regarding possible problem areas in their city and so forth, by that I mean if any information that reaches them is incomplete, they wouldn't know.'

Clem reached for his glass and drank the remainder of his whisky.

'The exact details have not been processed yet,' he continued, putting down the empty glass. 'There's still a great deal to work at. You'll all be informed as to your roles nearer the time. I suggest you all leave Mexico at different times from different exits to different places. I'll delegate that to Dave. He'll fix that up.' Clem again looked over at Ferrie, who nodded.

The Cuban sat near the doorway said, 'Why don't we get the President's brother, Bobby? He is the problem,' He took a long drag on his 'cigarette'.

'What the hell you got there?' Ferrie almost screamed. 'I thought I told you to keep a clear head tonight?'

'You drink, amigo, I smoke.'

Ferrie's eyes blazed at the Cuban who, in turn, stared right back. Ferrie approached him, ready to fight. The girl rose from the chair and stood between the Cuban and Ferrie.

'No!,None of this! I haven't come here for this!'

Ferrie backed off, glaring at the Cuban. Clem stood, his towering body rising quickly.

'Dave … enough. Let's keep our heads …'

Ferrie turned and returned to his drink, burying his face into the glass of whisky.

… crazy Ferrie … crazy boy …

The atmosphere remained strained until the white guy who had entered with Ruby and Clem pushed himself off the wall and said, 'Because if we get Bobby, the whole world would come down on us. To stop a dog wagging its tail, you just don't cut the tail off. The dog will bite you. You shoot the fucker in the head. Then the tail stops as well.'

The entourage laughed. Oswald forced a grin.

… how poetic …

The Cuban's laugh ended with a beaming smile. He returned to his reefer, slumping back into the corner with his colleague. The two exchanged some quiet Spanish patter.

Ruby spoke, lifting his countenance to face his colleagues in crime, speaking in his high pitched voice from behind heavy rimmed glasses. 'If we do move to Dallas, if the Miami thing doesn't happen, I've organized a couple of places where the hit teams can stay.' Ruby paused, put his glass down onto the floor and clasped his ringed hands together, tightly.

'They will be quite safe. Obviously, I'll need to know more details around the time,' he then picked up his glass again and took a long drink, swallowed hard, sat back into the uncomfortable chair.

'What about weapons?' inquired Billy.

'We'll get to that later. You probably have a preference, so talk to Jack about that,' said Clem. 'Right now, we're still getting support from various groups in and out of the country.'

'Foreigners are in on this?' asked Lee.

'Out of the country doesn't necessarily mean foreigners. You people don't need to know those details, anyhow. You're in on the grass roots level,' he paused for effect, then stabbed the air in front of him. 'You guys are doing the job.'

A silence fell on the group as they took in the enormity of their destiny.

Clem continued as he held his audience, 'You people, should the Miami hit be ruled out, which I doubt, you people will be responsible for the assassination of the most powerful man in the Western Hemisphere, if not the world. You are about to enter history as Grand Redeemers. You are all about to become John Wilkes Booth. And, like him, you will not be apprehended.'

Ferrie held up his glass. 'John Wilkes Booth!' he said triumphantly. A chorus of toasts erupted from the group.

Billy turned to Oswald, beer can held high and looked him directly in the eye. Oswald in turn looked back at Billy.

'The memory of John Wilkes Booth!' Billy echoed Ferrie's sentiment.

'Booth,' muttered Oswald, beer can clanking against Billy's.

12

The bus journey from Mexico City had been a long, boring and mundane one. A bone-shaking, twenty-three hours of dust, dirt and thirst. Quick stops, longer waits for the driver at various points. Conversations with bores travelling through Mexico, Central America, the world. Having successfully deposited Ferrie's package at the bus station in Waco only an hour before, Lee Oswald stepped off the Greyhound bus at Lamar Street station in downtown Dallas and walked wearily to the luggage hatch. He was wearing the same shirt from the day before he left, not daring to go to the local Laundromat for fear of being seen by Ferrie or, more likely, one of his cohorts.

Lee stank. The sweetness of his body odor did not concern him directly, one got accustomed to one's own smell, but several of the passengers had been offended by his presence on the sweltering bus. Lee could care less. He was finally on his way home to Marina and the children, back to Dallas and the end of this whole nasty business. Ferrie and his friends would be taken care of, just as soon as Lee managed to contact Bishop. The plans he had witnessed during the eventful trip to Mexico City had at first amused him, then mystified him, then terrified him. To think that there were always people walking around, plotting robbery and murder had never occurred to him before. Mad dogs always roam in packs, history could testify to that. Lee tried to imagine the elation that such people as Chancellor-to-be Adolph Hitler must have felt when he met a like minded group that ultimately became responsible for the deaths of more than twenty million human beings.

... twenty million dead ...

Lee couldn't imagine that amount of people. All with family, all with a mother somewhere, brothers, sisters, a dog. People that would like to eat, sleep and love. All those tightly wrapped bundles of humanity, all with feelings and ideas and ambitions. Waiting to burst upon the world, to do something, to make a mark, however small or great that might be. Some of those people would have done bad things, most of them good. Writers, artists, musicians.

A thought passed his mind and he smiled.

... and I want to work for the Space Program ... spacecraft designed and constructed by the flotsam of Nazi Germany ... scientists spirited out of a defeated Germany to the United States ... to work for the American Government ... the spoils of war ... Twenty million dead, murdered by a madman and now that madman's top scientists working for the liberators of that country . . .

The past few days came back to him, days of frustration and hopelessness. The meetings, the discussions, the seriousness of it. Lee could feel himself becoming more and more depressed. He needed to see Marina and the children, to get something he cared for back into his life, to finish the awful charade in which he found himself – to sort out this web of deceit once and for all. But now the reality of it was staring him in the face. Beating him down and, ultimately, swallowing him. Whole.

To be a part in the shaping of history was probably everybody's dream. Lee's dream was rapidly turning into a nightmare. A voice disturbed his thoughts. It was his own.

'The blue zipper bag,' he said to the driver, automatically, 'here's my tag ...'

The driver, stood half bent at the side of the bus, glanced at Oswald's receipt, pulling the holdall out from the underbelly of the bus.

'There you go, fella,' he said, smiling. 'Long trip, huh? You look beat!'

'Thanks,' said Lee, sarcastically. He took the bag from the driver and walked away.

... can't go out to Irving tonight ... too far ... need to rest ... need a room for the night ...

Oswald stopped and put down his bag and leant against the bus depot wall on Lamar Street. A cooling breeze pushed its way around him, refreshing him, getting some of that dry Mexican dust out of from his lungs.

Lee hated Mexico. Mexico hated Lee.

... Mexico hates everybody, especially foreigners ...

It was afternoon and downtown Dallas was quiet, strange for a weekday but a change from the continual madness of the Mexican capital. Not many people were on the streets as far as he could tell, several cars drew slowly past, but he ignored their possible intent. He desperately needed sleep. The trip had lasted twenty-three hours and Lee had resisted the temptation of stopping in Laredo when he had to change buses, earlier that morning.

Lee had been annoyed that Ferrie would not fly him back to New Orleans or even to Dallas. The rest of them had done so, save him. Two twenty odd hour trips on the worst roads in the world within seven days was enough to sap anybody's strength. Still, he was happy to be away from them all now. Their plans laid, everything, accordingly to Ferrie, shipshape. Lee still could not believe what he'd heard during the past week.

... plans ... threats ... rifles ... modes of escape ...

The long Greyhound trip to Mexico from New Orleans, again the others had flown, his stay in the run down part of Mexico City, the endless meetings, being told to say nothing by Ferrie and Clem, listening to them conspire to murder the Chief Executive, speaking in great detail of triangulation of gunfire and availability of exits, all delivered in Ferrie's drawl, had sent chills up and down his spine on more than one occasion.

Ferrie, Lee was convinced, was quite mad, evil. Not a raving lunatic, but cold, calculating and capable. That frightened Lee the most. The cold manner in which Ferrie had discussed shooting the President on the streets, in cold blood, probably with his wife next to him...

He had to get to Bishop as soon as possible, but also had now to be more careful than ever. Being part of the 'plot', his association with these anti-Castro nut cases and his activities that summer would confuse any investigator as to his true loyalties and he may end up in deep trouble, to say the least.

...but Bishop will know... would put the record straight... but how to get to him ...

Oswald had not spoken to him for many months and had not been expecting to, leaving Bishop to contact him. Reaching into his pant's pocket, Lee pulled out five dollars and change. Looking down at the paltry sum in the palm of his hand, Oswald sighed heavily. All that money Clem and Ferrie had given him was back in New Orleans, sat in a box in the station. He couldn't spend the damn stuff, here he was, virtually penniless, hungry and weary, a fortune sat in a city hundreds of miles away . . .

... looks like the YMCA tonight ... I can register there as a serviceman and not have to pay the registration fee ...

Oswald smiled to himself and picked up his bag and walked into the bus station looking for the Information Desk.

*

'Hi! It's Lee!'

'Lee! You are back? Where are you?'

Marina's voice was a much-needed tonic to Oswald's lonely mood. Oswald stood leaning against the run down corridor in the Dallas YMCA building. Paint old and peeling, Lee brushed the leadened dye from his bare arm, angrily. Glancing up and down the corridor, Lee noticed the steam room entrance and silently figured he'd pay a visit.

'Well, I'm at the YMCA in Dallas. I got back in yesterday. I didn't call you because it was late. I've... missed you. And Junie.'

Marina glowed. 'Yes, we have all missed you also. We are all fine. The new baby is coming soon, on your birthday, I hope! When will I see you?'

'Well, as soon as you can get here. I'm on Mockingbird,' Lee looked at the small change in his hand, flipping two coins over and over.

'You want us to get you?' said Marina, seemingly backing away from the idea, hostility creeping into her voice.

Oswald frowned, 'Yeah, easiest way. Tell Ruth and come and pick me up!' He pulled the phone receiver away from his ear and looked at it.

'...no, Lee, I can't do that. Ruth can't pick you up,' Marina sounded different, her mood swinging away from her eagerness to see her husband.

'Why not?' Puzzled.

Marina snapped back, almost without thinking, 'Because it wouldn't be right to ask her, would it?'

'Why not?'

Another answer, just quick, wounding him just as deeply, 'It ... it would ... because it would be a burden.'

'...'

'Lee? Are you there?' Marina's voice sounded quizzical.

Oswald sighed. 'Yes, I'm here. Looks like I'm gonna be here a whole lot longer, too,' he finished, sarcastically.

His wife's tone calmed somewhat, as she said, 'Lee. Listen, you can get the bus... can't you?'

Oswald again looked at the change in his hand, not flipping the coins now, letting them rest poorly in his palm.

He paused, hoping for a lasting effect.

'Marina, I haven't got any money...' The pause did not work and he felt low again. 'I'll see you later, presuming it is okay for me to come out there?' Oswald was almost pleading by now.

Marina gave him nothing and spoke stingingly. 'Don't take that tone, Lee... Ruth has put herself out enough for you in the past. I'll tell her you are on your way... Lee?'

Oswald was distant, '... yeah.'

'How long will you be?'

'Well, I have no money, it's only about fifteen miles from downtown Dallas to you... carrying my bags and all... I should be able to walk it in about–'

Marina hung up.

Oswald felt depressed as he searched his pockets for another ten cents. He was low on cash, never mind change. He fingered his way through the coins and at last found the elusive dime.

Lee thought about the last conversation he'd had with David Ferrie, the day before he set off for Dallas from Mexico City.

'Remember Lee, don't forget to do the drop in Waco, you know about the post box - drop the parcel in there ... brown parcel ... don't forget, whatever you do...'

yeah, yeah, fag ... well, I didn't forget ...

'and don't forget to get in touch with Ruby when you get back into Dallas'

... Ruby, jeeps and girls ...

'ring him at the Carousel, don't leave your name if he's not there ... call back ... don't go and see him ...you need to meet with him ... maybe he'll be a little vague, remind him of who you are ... he has your instructions ... get to see him, it's vital that you see him, do what he says ... remember, he's a forgetful sonofabitch so remind him ... go to him, see him ...'

Lee pulled the receiver back off the hanger and dropped the tiny coin into the slot. Dialling the number from memory, Lee waited patiently as the call was placed.

'Carousel Club.' The voice seemed dark.

'Jack Ruby, please,' Lee said, tonelessly.

'Who's calling, please?'

'Jack Ruby, please.'

The voice on the other end of the line seemed to understand. A moments pause, then, 'One moment, please.'

Oswald heard the owner of the dark voice place his hand over the mouth piece, the muffling sound quite evident. Lee heard some other garbled sounds as the piece was obviously being passed to someone else.

'Hello?' The voice had changed. Even over the phone, Lee could place Ruby to the high, squeaky tones.

'Jack Ruby, please.'

'Who is this?'

Oswald smiled as he visualized Ruby getting worked up,

ready to burn his short fuse in a second.

'Jack, I just got in from Mexico City ...'

'Mex ... who the hell is this? Come on, speak to me!'

'Alex Hidell, Jack.'

There was a pause. Lee looked into the mouthpiece and tried in vain to see Ruby's face down the telephone cord.

'Jack ...'

'Yes. Yes, I heard you. I can't talk to you now,' Ruby was distracted by a female voice and Lee wondered if his dime would run out and he'd lose the call.

... come on, damn you ...

'... and get Larry to bring up some more beers, uh, yeah, uh, Alex! Sorry. Look, come by my place next week, call me next week, okay?'

'Here or your apart–'

'Yeah, bye now.'

Click.

Lee slammed the receiver back onto its hanger.

Goddam!

Oswald decided to write up the events of the previous week in Mexico, open a new Post Office Box in Dallas and drop the information in it. He knew that it would make pretty good reading for somebody at the Bureau, and he longed for Bishop to get in touch with him, soon.

Lee paused long enough in the telephone booth to consider that Bishop was not receiving his tip–offs.

That scared him.

... all the information that I've carefully collated during the summer and the past week must have been getting through ... there has to be someone acting on this information ... hell ... it's so damned important ...someone must be working on it ... why me ... why did I get mixed up in all this ... damn Ferrie and his weirdo faggot cronies ... murderers, walking the streets, waiting for the President to arrive ... and who were the other infiltrators of the group ... if only I could talk to someone who could understand the way I feel ...

Lee knew to walk into the local FBI office would have been the worst thing he could do in these circumstances. Even if the officers there were to talk with him, the same ones who did know of his whereabouts and monitored him regularly, they'd still think he was the crank who defected to Russia for two and a half years. They would not listen to him.

... Bishop is the only answer ... but where is he ...

Lee tried to let the thought go.

... can't deal with this right now ... I need a place to stay. I'll go and see Marina and stay there tonight ...

Oswald's spirits ebbed and showed no sign of rising. Grabbing his bag from his room at the 'Y', he walked slowly into Dealy Plaza, its open lawns making him feel only slightly better. As he walked down Main Street toward the Stemmonds Freeway, Lee glanced to his right at the old, red bricked building adorned with a gigantic Hertz RentaCar sign on top of it. The building meant nothing to Lee and he turned to face forward, walking briskly under the triple underpass hoping to find a willing citizen, Irving and Marina bound.

*

'So, you went to New Orleans just to get work?' Captain Fritz asked.

'That's right,' answered Lee, memories of the summer flashing by in his mind's eye, 'and to visit some relatives I have there.'

'Were you successful in looking for work?' Agent Bookhout interjected.

Oswald looked at him, still figuring how to get to talk to this agent in private.

'Oh, yes. I knew I'd find something,' said Lee. 'I also went back there because that's where I'm from, originally. I hadn't been there since I left the country in fifty-nine.'

'To go to Russia?'

Oswald eyed Hosty. 'Uh, huh.'

Another rattle on the door as a uniform stepped into the office. Fritz looked and waved the officer over to him. The officer passed the chief a large manila envelope.

'From the lab, Captain,' said the officer as the Chief took the envelope and opened it.

'Thank you, Brown. That's all for now.'

'Sir,' the officer spun on his heel and left the interrogation room.

Oswald's gaze fell on the Captain, busy peering into the envelope.

'Mister Hosty, I think that you'll want to see these...' Fritz waved the FBI man over to him. Hosty peered over the Captain's shoulder as Fritz pulled out several large black and white photographs and set them on the desk in front of them.

Oswald leant forward in an attempt to see what they were. Lee immediately recognized the head of the individual in the two photos.

It was him.

Lee frowned as Hosty and Fritz remained silent, looking closely at the images.'

'Mister Oswald,' said Fritz, slowly, 'I think you'll need to see these ...'

Fritz spun the photos around to enable his prisoner to see them. Lee picked up the top photo and looked closely at it. It showed someone posing with a rifle and revolver, and holding a newspaper.

...that's my face but ...

'Well, Oswald?' said Hosty, almost triumphantly, as he moved away from the Captain, 'what do you make of these?'

Fritz looked at Oswald, cold eyed, 'You got anything you want to say about these?'

...it's not me ... it's my face ... on someone else's body ... but it's not me with this hardware ...

'That's my face, but it's not me. These photos have been faked.'

Oswald looked at both photos carefully. One showed a person with a rifle held in the right hand with the butt resting on the individual's hip. In this same photo, the individual was holding a newspaper in his left hand and a revolver and holster completed the one-man arsenal. In the background were some steps to an upper floor of a building that Oswald thought he remembered.

The second photo showed him and the weapons even more clearly, alongside the same steps.

'Why should they have been faked?' Hosty enquired.

'How the hell do I know...' Oswald snapped, 'but if you think hard, it becomes pretty clear.'

Fritz asked, 'You think they're fakes then. Why?'

Oswald looked at the Captain and carefully measured his answer, speaking slowly and clearly. 'Someone has put my face on these photos. The face is mine, but that's not my body,' Lee tapped the photo with his finger, 'someone has superimposed my face on to someone else's body.'

'Well, Lee,' said the Captain, 'some of my officers have just found these pictures in the Paine's garage, in one of your seabags.'

Oswald slammed the desk with his fist. 'Dammit, Fritz, those pictures have never been in my possession! They're fakes! Someone is trying to set me up, don't you see?' Lee sat back into his chair, anger painted over his face.

The Captain continued. 'This photo is an enlarged version of some smaller ones we found, as I said, at the Paine's garage.'

'So, there is some dispute regarding the originals? Then which were found, the smaller ones or these?'

'We found these smaller ones, Fritz skimmed the smaller photos across the desk to Lee. He studied them carefully.

'Did you find the negatives?' Lee said, almost in a whisper

as he poured over the details depicted in the pictures.
'That I can't say, Lee.'
'I've never seen these photos before now,' Oswald found it difficult to keep his temper under control, 'I don't know anything about them, other than that they're fakes.' Oswald pushed the photos back onto the desk in contempt. 'Listen, I've done a lot of photography and I know what I'm talking about. This smaller picture is a reduction from the larger, it's that obvious, but I did not make it. Somebody else had to do it.
'I've been photographed a million times since you brought me here and I've been photographed in the corridor between offices. Someone obviously has been able to get my photo and with that,' he paused and shrugged, 'they made this picture.'
'Well, that's interesting,' said Hosty.
Oswald looked over at the FBI agent. 'It sure is. I know photography real well and given time I'll prove that those pictures are forgeries.'
'How would you explain the forged Service card in your wallet, the one with your picture on it but the name Hidell?' said Hosty folding his arms.
Oswald looked at him, scornfully. 'You won't be able to tie that Service Card in with these pictures, so don't even try.'
'Tell us about that card, Lee,' said Fritz, putting the photos back into the envelope. 'Tell us all you can ...'
Oswald smiled. 'You think I'm gonna fall for that? Give me a break. Listen, I refuse to answer any more questions. You people are denying me my constitutional rights. I won't say any more until my attorney has been contacted.'
Captain Fritz turned to one of his detectives. 'Jim, take Mister Oswald to the fourth floor. His wife and mother are waiting to see him.'
Oswald stared in disbelief, his mouth dropping open.

*

Marina Oswald and Lee's mother, Marguerite, sat huddled together on the other side of the glass. Lee saw them as he was led into the dimly lit wooden booth by a uniform. Oswald sat on the only chair and noticed that it had been bolted to the floor. Behind him, he first felt the draft and then heard the noise of the door being shut behind him and the turn of the key locking it secure. Oswald turned to face the two women.

Marina was sobbing into her handkerchief while his mother held her and the baby. Oswald's mother saw him first and her mouth gaped open as she saw her injured son's face. Peering at him through her horn-rimmed glasses, Lee's mother's tears fell down her cheeks.

'Lee …' was all she could say.

Marina looked up, sharply. As Lee's wife saw him she began to weep even more, shaking her head from side to side, lips trembling, her eyes rolling.

Oswald looked at her and tried to smile, to give them both some indication of his innocence and that despite his facial bruises, he was in good health.

'Mom,' he said through the glass. He knew she couldn't hear him. Lee picked up the phone receiver hanging on the wall and held it to his ear. Marina saw this and snatched the other phone from her mother-in-law's grasp.

'Lee! Lee! What is happening? Why are you here? The police …' Marina spoke quickly in Russian and Oswald's mother looked on in bewilderment. Lee tried quickly to calm his almost hysterical wife.

'I'm okay, Marina,' he answered quickly, if not reassuringly. 'I'm fine. I'll be out of here soon, don't worry …'

The Russian girl shook her head, her pretty face wet with distress. 'No, Lee. They say you are guilty. They told us you shot John Kennedy.'

'Marina,' interrupted Oswald, 'I didn't shoot anybody. I'm not guilty of anything.'

Lee paused as her face crumbled before him. He desperately wanted to touch her, hold her, but the charges, and the glass, prevented him. The prisoner pressed his hand flat against the glass pane. Marina did the same.

'Now, let me talk to my mother.'

Marina looked stunned at this, then understood. She passed the phone to Marguerite.

'Lee-' she said, but was cut off by Oswald.

Sternly, he said, 'Mom, you must keep Marina under your wing. She needs you badly,' Oswald's mother was already nodding her head in agreement. 'I doubt she can get through this on her own. They'll put pressure on her and she'll need someone,' Lee looked his mother straight in the eye. 'Don't let me down on this, mom,' For the first time in a long while, Lee Oswald was depending on his mother for some kind, any kind, of support.

'I won't, Lee. I won't let her out of my sight. I promise. I won't let you down.'

Oswald nodded then said, 'Put Marina back on, please.'

Marguerite passed the phone back to Marina and he spoke to her in Russian again. She smiled weakly as she lifted the receiver to her ear, lips trembling, tears still filling her beautiful green eyes.

'Marina, I love you more than you'll ever know. I never wanted you to leave and go and live at Ruth's,' said Oswald quietly, fixing his stare with hers, 'but let's not worry about that now. I'll be out of here soon, then we can sort things out. Now, where is Junie?' he inquired.

'Junie is with Ruth, she's been good to us all, Lee. She is not as bad as you think she is.'

Oswald smiled again.

...I'll hold judgment on that ....

'Look after my mother, Marina. She needs you.'

'I will, Lee. We all love you,' she said quietly. 'We will do our best to get you out.'

'I know you will,' Oswald looked at Marina's hair. Dragged back from her face, untidy and tied in a bun at the back of her head.

... still, it doesn't hide her lovely face ...Marina, twenty two years old and looking like an old woman ...sat here before me, because I got mixed up in something ... over my head ... over my head and now this ...

Oswald felt tears welling in his eyes and inhaled deeply through his nose to stop them falling, a lump forming in his throat. The phone was becoming sweaty in his grasp. A faint odor of tobacco drifted from it.

'Lee,' said Marina, looking into his eyes, 'what are you doing in here? Why you?' she pleaded.

'Marina, I can't explain now. One day, I will, but not now.'

Lee wanted to tell them both about Bishop and everything else, but stopped himself. They had enough on their minds.

At that moment, the door behind Lee opened and he turned to see a policeman standing in the frame.

'That's it, Oswald. Time's up, buddy.'

The cop stood back from the door. Oswald caught a glimpse of the police officer's colleague in the corridor outside.

'Okay,' he said, turning back to the women, 'Marina, I have to go now.'

'No, Lee, stay with us,' cried Marina, putting her hand on the glass again.

Lee half stood and put his palm over Marina's, feeling the glass separating them. It may as well have been a hundred miles thick. As he moved away, Oswald was overcome by the immense tide of emotion he held behind his eyes, 'Look after the children...'

'You're the best father in the world, Lee,' Marina said into the phone as Oswald began to hang up. 'You're the best-'

she shouted, but the words were lost somewhere in the wooden booth.

Oswald left the booth without looking back.

… I'll be out of here soon and this thing will all be over …

Part Three
Oblivion

Oblivion

As the cop opened the cell door, Lee Oswald opened his eyes. He'd been awake for about an hour after another restless night. His first thoughts when he awoke, as the Dallas dawn filtered through the barred window above him, was one of a peaceful silence. As his head cleared and the enormity of his circumstance fell like a wave over him, Lee realized that today he would make his statement. Whoever was there in the room with him, whoever learned of his place in all this mess and the exposure of his cover, well, they would know too. Though he didn't feel he had been mistreated physically, Oswald knew the police were depriving him of counsel and had, it was obvious, already convinced themselves and the watching world of his overwhelming guilt.

Lee understood why.

A police department's role in the great scheme of things was to appease public anger of any crime, however heinous it might be. The police, he knew, were as confused about the events of this weekend as he was, probably more so and for that reason, he could not attach too much blame on their actions ... until he allowed himself to think about it. He lifted his head from the pillow and saw the cop standing over him.

'Wakey, wakey, boy,' said the cop. 'Time for you to eat breakfast. You got around ten minutes before we come back for you.'

Lee rubbed the sleep from his eyes and mumbled an acknowledgement. Turning over onto his back, Oswald watched the cop head out the jail door, pull his keys, turn and lock him in again.

Despite his incarceration, and the fact that locked doors prevented his freedom, Lee felt most secure in the cell with the door locked. He knew that no one could get to him in here. The corridors of the building were a different thing. What frightened him the most was walking down to the Captain's office.

... anyone could be in that crowd ...

He shuddered as he sat up, pulling away the single blanket. Swinging his legs over the edge of his cot, the blanket fell to the floor. He watched the brown cloth fall into an untidy heap. Lee firmly planted his feet onto the cold, hard floor of the cell. The Arctic feeling through his feet helped wake him up, clearing his head of his warm, sleepy bed.

Lee slowly looked around the grimy plaster walls of the cell. Yet again, a wave of depression fell over him as he thought of Marina and the kids. Although it was only three days since he'd played with Junie and Rachael, Oswald felt he'd been deprived of their company by actions beyond his control and a certain bitterness mingled with the depression.

He exhaled loudly.

Standing, he stretched his arms out to release the last residues of slumber and felt better for it. Lee pulled on his trousers, socks and shoes and moved over to the toilet. As he sat, Lee held his head in his hands and closed his eyes. He'd finally managed to stop every thought regarding the assassination flooding into his tortured mind and could think rationally about the days gone by.

His mind went back to the Soviet Union and his 'defection' just four years earlier.

... who was I working for, he thought ... Agency ...Naval Intelligence ...

He didn't know. It was impossible to know. Maybe it was the Soviet KGB.

A smile touched his face at that thought.

That's ludicrous, of course ...

Lee tossed the images of his arrival on a cold Moscow day from his mind. Russia always brought him back to Marina and, strangely, his mother. Marguerite Oswald had never had time for Lee and his brothers during their childhood years, always getting in her way, she having to drag them around every place. Lee remembered the fights he'd been in at various schools in New York, he'd always been the 'gray belly' they 'the yankees'. He smiled again as he finished with the commode.

A rattle on the bars made him jump. The cop had returned.

'You ready now?'

'Yes, sir,' replied Lee. He moved to the bed, picked up his T-shirt and put it on as the cop rattled his keys in the lock and pulled the jail door open.

'Breakfast first, then you can shower if you want to. You're being moved today.'

Oswald turned sharply to the policeman, 'Where? Where to?' he said, excited at the prospect. The cop backed off, knowing he'd said too much already. 'You'll see.'

Oswald looked at the policeman. The older man relented, looked around and spoke in a soft Texan drawl.

'County Jail, so I heard. Not that far away.'

'Yeah,' said Lee, tucking in his shirt as he passed through the jail door into the barred corridor area. 'I work near there...'

The cop looked at him and was joined by a colleague. The second policeman stared hard at Oswald and rested one hand on his hip and the other on his revolver as it nestled snugly in its holster. 'Oswald, did you really do this?'

The two policemen waited eagerly for Lee's reply. He looked at them both.

'No, sir,' Lee straightened his shirt. 'No, I didn't.'

'Then what the hell are you doin' in here?'

Oswald glanced at them both, a certain pleading in his eye, then pursed his lips and looked away.

'You tell me,' he whispered. Then silence fell on them all and the cops looked at each other, a puzzled look on their faces.

'Okay,' said one. 'Breakfast.'

*

'Okay, Lee, take a seat and we'll just go over a few more things before you go to the County Jail lock-up.'

Captain Fritz motioned to Oswald as he appeared, handcuffed, at the officer's door. Lee walked in and sat in the corner. Fritz stood and walked slowly around the room, saying, 'I'll get the introductions over with quick as I can. This is Tom Kelley of the United States Secret Service,' Oswald remembered all the faces from the previous day.

He glanced at them as they all stared at him.

The Captain continued his introductions, pacing the office floor and pointing at the individuals in question. He continued.

'This is Postal Inspector Holmes ... FBI Agent in Charge Sorrels and these are members of the Dallas Homicide Squad.'

No-one spoke, no one smiled and no one nodded. A feeling of intense formality shrouded the interior of the room and Lee's mood changed like the wind. Since hearing that he was to be moved the short distance to the County Jail, just south of the Book Depository in Dealy Plaza, Oswald figured any more interviews were useless. Still, he mused, let the old guy get on with it.

'Now, Lee,' said Fritz returning to his chair, 'you probably remember these pictures.' The Captain pulled open one of his drawers and produced a large brown envelope. He tossed it over to Oswald.

'In there, you'll find some photos of yourself holding the assassination rifle, the pistol that you shot Officer Tippit with and some communist papers. Take a look ...'

'I'm not picking up anything ... if you want to show me something, then show me,'

'Well, that's not a nice way to talk, you understand,' the Captain peered at Oswald over his eyeglasses.

'Well, I'm damn sure you people aren't here to be nice to anyone. I didn't shoot anyone,' protested Oswald again, slamming his fists onto the desk top, 'and as far as I'm concerned, you people have brought me here because I popped a policeman on the nose in the theater on Jefferson Avenue. I'm not touching anything.'

Captain Fritz continued. 'Well ... let's see, now. It would save this police department a whole lot of trouble if you would just tell us where these photos were taken-'

Oswald barely kept his rising anger at bay. 'I told you,' he said through gritted teeth, trying to suppress the scream he felt welling up inside of him. 'That's not me in those damn pictures. It's my head, but not my body.'

Lee sat back into the chair and glanced around the office.

'Yes, you did say that yesterday,' Fritz spoke quietly, picked up the envelope and spilled the contents out onto the desk in front of Lee. The accused looked down on the so-called evidence, scattered randomly before him. It was obvious to Lee that his head had been superimposed onto the body holding the rifle and pistol. He could even make out the faint line below his lip where the joining had occurred.

'Then you know the answer,' said Lee, thinking if it weren't so serious, he'd laugh at the amateurism displayed in the photographs, 'I refuse to answer anything relating to those fake photos. Go ahead and ask me all you want about them. But I won't answer.'

He looked down at the floor, avoiding all eye contact.

'Okay, Lee. Tell us why you opened the post office boxes

here in Dallas,' Fritz pulled a fresh note pad from his desk drawer and began to write on it.

'That's easy. I rented a box for several months before moving to New Orleans. There is no federal offense that I know of that prevents me from renting a post office box. That's what they're for. I opened the box in my own name and you can check that. I have two keys, which I think you'll find normal. When I closed the box, I had the mail forwarded to my address in New Orleans. It was easier to do this than to inform all the publishers and so on of a change of address. At least two of the papers I subscribed to are published in Russia, one of them from Minsk, the town where I met my wife.'

The Captain stopped writing and looked up at Oswald. 'You seem to move around a lot, just what were you up to?'

Oswald ignored him. 'No-one received any mail in any of my boxes and I did not receive any mail in any other name but my own. You can check all that ... if you haven't already.'

Holmes, the Postal Inspector said, 'We found your wife's name on the application of people allowed to pick up mail from your box.'

Lee sniggered. 'Of course, I may have given my wife a key to get stuff for me, but there's no law against that. But nobody else. I emphatically deny I ordered a rifle or revolver to that box under any name, including my own, nor did I permit anyone else to order those weapons to my box. Further, while we're on this track yet again, I wholeheartedly deny that I even considered buying a mail order rifle from anyone. I have not fired a rifle since I left the Marines.' Lee held his hands up under his chin. 'How could I afford to order a rifle on my salary of one dollar twenty five cents an hour when I can hardly feed myself on what I make?' He slowly shook his head.

Kelley said. 'It also states one Alek Hidell as being a recipient of mail.'

Lee shrugged. 'I don't recall anything about that,' he lied. After a short pause, he continued. 'When I got back from New Orleans and after I got the job at the BookStore, I opened a box at the nearby Terminal Annex Postal Building. This box was opened in my name only,' Lee stated, emphatically.

Fritz joined in the crossfire. 'We have reason to believe you put 'Fair Play for Cuba Committee' on the, uh, application form for that box, as well as 'American Civil Liberties Union'. Why was that?'

Oswald shrugged and looked away, saying, 'I don't recall putting that information on any form.'

'Could you tell us who paid for the box rental?' said Holmes, folding his arms.

'Sure,' answered Lee, 'that's simple enough,' Oswald looked him straight in the eye.' ... Me.'

'Did, or does anyone else know about this particular post office box?' The questions began to arrive thick and fast.

...Moscow ...

'Only you,' he said, quietly.

'Nobody else outside this office?'

'Only you.'

Kelley began pacing the office again, looking down at the floor as he did so. 'How long have you been a member of the Civil Liberties Union?'

Oswald's answers became automatic.

...do they really think they're gonna shake me...

'I repeatedly made efforts to join that Union, but I was never sure of my application. I waited and waited for some kind of papers or identification, but nothing ever came through. As far as I am concerned, I paid my dues, five bucks, so I'm a member.'

'How did you become interested in your work with Cuba?' said Kelley, removed his jacket to reveal a neat waistcoat beneath. After hanging up his jacket, Kelley leant against the door.

Oswald looked at him, and, feeling he could answer Kelley's questions, spoke with a new confidence.

… as long as they don't get into the assassination area …

'I did no official work for Cuba, okay? Don't confuse that with being, uh, an agent for Cuba or anything like that … I am not part of, ah, a cell that opened up in Dallas. I work purely on my own. I just happen to be an American who believes that we, we being the United States, Cuba and the Cuban government should have free intercourse, or to put it another way, full diplomatic relations with each other. Cuba and the United Sates can, and should, strike up some kind of relationship, whether it be trade or just dialogue'

Kelley spoke quietly as he moved away from the door and stood behind the Captain.

'Lee, do you think that the assassination of President Kennedy will have any effect on the Fair Play for Cuba situation?' Kelley raised his eyebrows and Oswald could see he was genuinely interested in what Lee's answer might be.

Lee thought for a moment, dropping the sides of his mouth as he did so. 'I doubt there will be a massive change in attitude of the American people toward Cuba with Johnson as President,' Lee stated, shrugging his shoulders. 'After all, Kennedy and Johnson do belong to the same political party, so, no, I don't see any change there. One will surely follow the other on the previous stand.' Oswald looked Kelley in the eye, said, 'Let me ask you a question.'

'Go ahead.'

'Are you with the FBI?'

Kelley looked puzzled. 'No, I'm with the Secret Service,' he replied.

'Mm …' continued Oswald, 'after the shooting, when I left work, I stood around talking with some of the guys for a couple of minutes. As I decided to go home, as I was walking from the Bookstore, a young crew-cut man rushed up to me and said he was from the Secret Service and asked me where a phone was. I told him, I pointed to the main doorway of the Bookstore, the phones being through there and I watched him go in.'

Kelley leant forward and supported himself on Fritz's desk.

'Did you believe him, when he told you he was from the Secret Service?'

'Sure. He pushed a book of identification under my nose.'

Kelley looked puzzled for a moment. Oswald watched him.

... *nothing to do with anything ... but wouldn't the Secret Service stay with the president ...*

'Oswald, as a Marxist, do you believe that religion is, er, an opiate for the people?'

... *interesting question ...*

Oswald nodded. 'Sure, very definitely. And so, because of this, all religions tend to become monopolistic and so forth and sometimes become the cause of a great deal of class warfare ... considering all this, I would like to state that if I have a religion, it would be Karl Marx. I have read everything there is to read by, or about, Karl Marx. Some people find the Bible interesting reading and that's fair enough, but it's not for me. Even as a philosophy, there isn't much to the Bible.'

Kelley continued. 'Do you consider the Catholic Church to be an enemy of the Communist philosophy?'

... *this guy knows his stuff ...*

'Well, as you are probably aware, there is no Catholicism in Russia, the closest to it would be, uh, the Orthodox Churches ...'

Oswald stopped, mid-sentence, sat back in his chair and smiled at Kelley. 'I can't discuss this with you anymore,' he said, dragging a thumb across his lower lip.

Kelley was stunned by Oswald's sudden change of demeanor.

'Why not?' he said, a puzzled mask falling onto his face.

Kelley stood away from the desk, as Oswald spoke directly at him.

'Because I feel that this is an attempt to have me say something against the Catholic Church, or something anti-religious.'

Kelley laughed sarcastically and held his hands up in surrender as his eyes rolled to the heavens. He began to shake his head.

Captain Fritz, scratching his temple with his pencil brought Oswald and Kelley back to the matter at hand, 'we understand from our background that you were dishonorably discharged from the Marines. Evidently, this had something to do with your defection to Russia ...'

All in the office watched as Oswald momentarily bristled. They'd struck a chord. Oswald became visibly irritable, trying to evade his obvious embarrassment.

Oswald spoke sternly and deliberately.

'I was, in fact, discharged honorably from the Marine Corps however, the State Department and the Marine Corps changed the paperwork after I left for the Soviet Union. It was because I tried to denounce my American Citizenship whilst over there. And, while we're on this, I will tell you that I did write to Governor Connally when I came back and I explained to him that I did not denounce my citizenship and that, as he was Secretary of the Navy at the time, he should look into my case and have it changed.'

'The outcome?'

'I got a very nice letter stating that he had quit that post to run for Governor and that his office would pass my letter onto a Mister Cork, or Kurth, which I presume they did.'

'And you're still waiting,' questioned Holmes.

Oswald looked to the floor. 'Yes.'

Captain Fritz, aware that their little chat was over, brought them all back to the point in hand.

'Lee. Have you ever, or do you know of anyone who lived

in South Oak Cliff?'

'No, not to my knowledge, why South Oak Cliff? I've never even been there.'

*

After leaving the bus, Lee walked the few blocks to the Harlandale Street address Ruby had spoken of. It was a clear evening, a hint of the day's blue still hanging in the gathering darkness. Lee's mind had been on his family all that day, and he'd been preoccupied with it at work, much to the annoyance of his foreman, Bill Shelley. Shelley had found it necessary to point out to Oswald that, as he had only been employed at the Book Store these past couple of weeks, Lee had 'better watch his step', especially as one of the colored boys was on the look out for a job for his brother, recently in from Chicago.

Lee felt an urge to tell Shelley just what the hell he might do with his job and then do it again. He didn't. Oswald knew that his time here in Dallas was almost over and that he'd be moving back to New Orleans in a couple of weeks, after the President had left Texas safely.

A couple of weeks ... what more information can I give my contact ... and who is he anyway ... that note from Bishop telling of the change of plan sure sounded a little hokey ... but nothing I can do about it, until I'm away from here ... what the hell can Bishop be playing at, so close to Ferrie's operation ... and still no face to talk to ... Ruby, with the shifty eyes, looking deep into mine ... sometimes I think he's onto me ...

A cold chill ran the length of Lee's back and he stiffened momentarily in the soft Dallas breeze. Quickening his pace, Lee could see Ruby's car parked down from the house he was headed for.

Damn, all this mooching around on buses and taxis ... hell, Ferrie didn't even give me a flight back to Dallas... that blasted bus ride back from Mexico all but killed me...

Lee began to anticipate the evening's proceedings as best he could. Such things were not recommended in this kind of situation because all was unknown, but he couldn't settle his mind. Oswald was now only four houses down from the number Ruby had given him

... was it Ruby who had dropped the note in his Post Office Box... or ...

The house was similar in size to the rooming house where Lee stayed on Beckley. One of those 'well, it's seen better days but better is comin' again' dwellings. All the shutters were in place on the windows and Lee could see cracks of electric light escaping through them.

... lights on and it's not even dark yet ...

The Oak Cliff area in general was the pits side of town and Lee thought Beckley was bad. This place, the southern Oak Cliff area, positively smelt bad.

... no wonder Ruby has all of his safe houses down this side of the river ... who the hell in his right mind would come to a dump like this ...

Oswald smiled nervously. Here he was, alone in a strange, low-income area - a white male, walking through darkness that belonged to Mexican Immigrants. Lee's only consolation was his .38, nestled snugly in the waistband of his pants. He felt the revolver under his shirt, against his skin and was momentarily comforted.

Lee stopped at the kerb before the house and looked around. Not a person in sight. He felt as if he were in a ghost town, wished he were in a ghost town. Wished he was far away from this place, this place that unforeseen powers had sent him, that Jack Ruby had insisted he go to on this particular evening.

... in that house men are plotting murder, just as they were in Mexico ...

Although it had only been weeks since his return from those mind boggling meetings, Lee had tried to imagine the whole thing had been a dream. Instead, he'd been walking around in an almost dreamlike manner since returning to Dallas and hadn't everyone noticed it.

Even Ruth had commented, first to him, then to Marina, then to them both. Lee could not share the reason for this, but longed to tell someone, anyone...

... this is it...

He walked slowly up the garden path to the front porch, what's that crazy English thing;

... onward, onward, into the valley ... something ...

The porch door flew open, startling him, stopping him dead in his tracks. It was Ferrie, smiling and stinking.

'Hi, Lee! Good to see you!'

... were those the same damn fatigues he'd been wearing this whole summer and fall ...

Lee looked at him behind tired eyes. 'Hi, Dave,' he said, quietly.

Ferrie tipped his head, inquisitively. 'Anything wrong? You look like shit ...'

Oswald joined Ferrie on the porch step. 'Not really, just a dose of feeling sorry for myself, I guess. It's a long way from my place to here. Everybody seems to get here on their own wheels, or somebody else's.'

Lee turned away from Ferrie's gleaming eyes, not bothering to look again at his glue stained head, the shock of red monkey hair adorning his skull.

'Then you should learn to drive, Lee,' Ferrie paused, still looking onto Oswald's face, a look of genuine concern on his. 'You sure you're okay?'

Lee tipped his head back, pursing his lips and looked up at the heavens. 'Just melancholy. Thinking, hoping, some praying, all that kind of stuff...'

'Well,' said Ferrie putting his arm around Oswald's shoulder, 'If it's perking up you need, then let me tell you this,' Ferrie spoke quietly and looked back at the front door,

'Ruby's in there and he's shaking like a leaf,' Ferrie chuckled. 'Apparently, he's on tranquilizers. He's taken so many, when he gets up to go the bathroom, he rattles!'

Ferrie burst into a high-pitched giggle and Lee flashed a false smile. He felt like throwing up; he could smell Ferrie's odor.

'Also,' Ferrie continued, 'rumor has it, we're all getting an advance in salary tonight ...'

Oswald was not impressed. 'Well, that's something,' he said, sarcastically.

... just where and when am I gonna be able to spend it ...

The thought of even more cash lying in a Post Office box filled Oswald with more frustration, more than he thought he would be able to carry. His head swam, his nose felt like committing suicide and his legs wanted to walk all the way back to New Orleans.

... now ...

'We've been here all day, Jack and I,' Ferrie smiled gleefully, taking a long deep breath, catching the smell of the air. 'You should have seen him squirm when Alvin and I went into the back bedroom this afternoon, I thought he was going to die ...' Ferrie put his hands on his hips and looked up at the stars, at last beginning to twinkle in the falling blackness.

Lee looked sharply at Ferrie. 'Alvin?' he said.

'Yeah, he's a cute kid. Flew him up from New Orleans yesterday. He's nineteen and got the cutest blond hair ...'

'Where is he now? Does he have any-'

'No, he doesn't know anything, except that he likes my plane. He's downtown, staying at someplace. He and I are flying back to Baton Rouge tomorrow. Got a job on.'

'Anything I should know about?' Oswald snapped.

'My, my, we are touchy tonight, aren't we Lee? A little ... jealous maybe?' Ferrie sniggered like a small child, showing decaying teeth behind thin lips.

Oswald wanted to punch the old faggot out. 'Go to hell, Dave. Don't even joke about it.'

Lee pushed past Ferrie, pulled open the mosquito screen, then the door and walked into the house. Ferrie watched him go in, eyes wide, stuck on eyebrows high on his wrinkled forehead, pausing only for the merest second before following him in.

*

'Lee, this map,' said the Captain, producing a ragged copy of The Dallas Morning News, 'we found this in your effects out on Beckley, at your rooming house.' Fritz threw the paper over to his prisoner. 'As you can see, it's a map of Dealy Plaza,' Fritz pointed with his pencil, 'there's the BookStore. Can you explain why there's a mark on there?'

Lee Oswald was stunned. Eyes wide in disbelief, he leant over and picked up the paper, 'My God, don't tell me there's a mark near where this thing happened?'

Lee looked closely at the paper and remembered making the marks on it.

'Jeez...' he said in a low voice. Lee held his forehead, bringing both cuffed hands up to do so. Fritz stretched his arm again and pointed to the mark.

'I put a number of marks on it,' Lee began to ramble as he panicked, never taking his eyes of the newspaper, staring at its implication, feeling sick at the thought of a jury poring over it.

'What about the other marks on the map?' he pleaded, turning the newspaper to face his captors and pointing in several different places on the photograph. 'I was looking for work and marked the places where I went for jobs or where I had heard there were jobs... you can't be implying that those are...'

Oswald stopped. He was incriminating himself.

... God, there's enough of that going on without helping them

frame me ...

He tried to calm down.

... say no more about it ...

The arresting officers all gazed upon Oswald, cold eyed.

'I have nothing more to say,' Oswald lifted his head from the damning evidence before him, 'talk to my lawyer about it.'

Oswald ground clenched teeth behind tightly shut lips. Again, a bout of depression fell on him. Lee suddenly felt tired. He wondered if he might crack. Captain Fritz put the newspaper into an envelope, put it into the drawer in the desk. Quietly, he shuffled the photographs of the armed person back into the other envelope and placed that, too, into a drawer in the desk.

That done, the Captain took off his spectacles and cleaned them. Oswald looked up again into Fritz's own weary eyes. Whether Fritz was aware of Oswald searching into his mind was not evident to Lee. Slowly, as he had done all weekend, Fritz continued to portray no emotion except maybe a tinge of boredom toward his prisoner.

'Why did you return home on Thursday night. You already told us about some curtain rods ... was that the only reason?'

Lee took a long, deep breath. 'No,' he stated. 'I hadn't seen my family for almost two weeks. Of course, I was going to go out there that weekend, but I learned that Mrs. Paine was giving a party for the children at the weekend and I guess it sounded like a good idea to go and see them on the Thursday. They were having a houseful of neighborhood kids at the party and I didn't want to be around.'

'Why not?'

'Well...' Oswald recalled painfully his argument with Marina, though he was at a loss as to why they had argued.

... probably something to do with money or Ruth ... or both . . .

*

As they sat in Ruth's back garden after dinner, Lee looked across at Marina in a peaceful moment, caressing her with his eyes. Dinner had been far from cordial, Ruth never missing the opportunity to make Lee feel uncomfortable.

...this is my house, Lee Oswald, mine, and you're hardly anything but my guest here...

It was time to spoil the peace and straighten out his future, their future, before that same future was thrust upon them, mercilessly. Lee found it difficult though, to disturb this peace, the only peace he'd known in...

...how many months...

Marina was talking to the baby, cradled in her arms, smiling at her, rocking her gently.

...I love you, Marina ...

As Oswald thought this, Marina looked up at him, directly in the eye. The words in her mind did not immediately form on her tongue. She gazed at him and he saw her soul for the first time in along time, framed in an unguarded moment. Lee saw her as he knew she was, deep, deep down inside, as she had been in Minsk, as she had been before they moved to Dallas. A half smile touched her lips as he brought the glass of beer to his.

'Lee,' She spoke abruptly, rocking the baby a little more vigorously, a little nervously, 'you seem distant. What is on your mind? Tell me before Ruth gets back.'

Oswald continued to look at her. Marina had again swept her light brown hair back off her face and tied it in a bun. He preferred it down and around, but she would not listen to him. Marina's green eyes shone in the fast fading light.

'Talk to me, Lee,' a certain pleading was etched in her voice.

'I'll talk to you, Marina,' Lee said, abruptly, 'I'll talk to you any time you like. But you refuse to talk to me, especially when Ruth is around.'

'I do not want a scene in Ruth's house. This is her house. She has troubles with Michael.'

'Don't I know it. Listen, we've got to sort *us* out, Marina. Okay, Ruth and Michael aren't doing too well, but they've got to be the one's to fix it,' Oswald paused. 'Marina, we're in trouble, too. And being here doesn't help.'

'Shame on you, Lee Oswald. Ruth has been a good friend to us.'

Oswald shook his head. 'No, Marina. She's been a good friend to you. Not me. You.'

'And how do you help? You run off to New Orleans and Mexico and leave me and the little ones …' Marina choked on the last words, her eyes brimming with tears. Oswald wanted to go to her, but he knew she would rebuke him. He felt the block in his throat. It felt like a brick.

'So, what do we do?' Marina asked, throwing the situation back at him, as if it were a stupid, worthless thing.

'Why don't we start by living together? We can get somewhere now I have a job.'

'But for how long? How long before the FBI come and they let you go again? How many times is it now?'

Marina's voice was straining, almost hysterical, but still low enough not to carry on the slight evening breeze. The baby cried out and stopped just as abruptly. Marina looked down at Rachael and rocked her and shushed her.

'Marina, I want to be with you, but I'm no longer sure of your intentions. I'm not in the same league as Ruth or the others. I don't have all the material things they can offer you. They don't like me, but I like you. I don't care about them. I care about you. I care about us.'

Marina sobbed. 'I have been thinking about going back to the Soviet Union.'

Oswald was devastated.

'I never see you, Lee. You are always up to something.'

'What do you mean?'

'Lee, I am not stupid. I don't know what it is that you do, but I know you are up to something.'

Oswald changed the subject. 'We can get a place in Oak Cliff again, Marina. Near to my work.'

Marina sneered. 'Work. You cannot keep a job. When you have one, the pay is no good,' Marina bit her lower lip and rocked Rachael quickly, vainly trying to put her little finger into the dozing baby's mouth.

Oswald felt his face pinching. He looked away and then down at the lawn. 'Thanks. Thanks a lot.'

'Don't start with the self pity!' She scolded him. 'We have two children here! We need money!'

... four thousand dollars in the bus station ... more to come . . .

'We can hardly feed ourselves! What will we do?' Suddenly, Marina brightened. 'If you could get a better job,'

... NASA Base at Gentilly, New Orleans ...

'We could get our own house and enough things for the girls. Maybe even a washing machine!'

'Marina, please don't go on about the washing machine again! A damn washing machine is not important right now!'

Marina raised her head, as if to look down upon Oswald, to leave him squirming in the dusk. 'To me it is,' she said in an unusually calm manner. 'I won't live in Oak Cliff again. Neely Street was a poor, wretched place. I will not bring up my children in such a place. Minsk is a better place than Neely Street. We could live at Uncle Yuri's again, he has plenty of room and he says-'

Oswald's eyes darted at his wife's, catching her dead center as he leant forward in his chair, 'You've been in touch with Yuri? Why didn't you tell me?'

'The same reason that you don't tell me what you are up to in New Orleans,' Marina glared at him, eyes flashing, wider and wider, goading him, daring him, 'because I did not want you to know about it, because it is a secret to me, my secret, just as New Orleans is a secret to you.'

Marina pursed her lips, an action she mimicked from Lee.

Oswald sank. It was hopeless.

... all I want, all I have is drifting away from me ...she's going back to Russia, to stay with Uncle Yuri. With the girls ...

'What are you thinking again?' Marina erupted, 'You see? You are not here again! You are wrapped in your secrets! Well, let me tell you, I have my secrets and I shall wrap myself up tighter than you can!'

Oswald thought about bringing his hand up to his face, in an effort to rub his chin, but could not. He felt limp, inert. He didn't even have the strength to pick up his beer, let alone continue to argue with his tempestuous wife.

The sun was almost through for the day. It was a warm, comfortable night and Lee had thought the evening had gone reasonably well up until this little conversation, even with Ruth's biting comments. He was weary and beaten. Tomorrow, he would become a part of an as yet unknown future, rushing toward it with uncertainty. The President would drive happily past to his fund raising meeting at the Trade Mart, surrounded by unsuspecting guards and policemen, waving to the crowds, milking their approval. Jackie would be next to him, next to her husband. The Kennedys would be together, man and wife, as it should be.

Lee's demeanor was one of total dejection and rejection. He was twenty-four years old and his life so far had meant nothing. His career seemed to have gone on hold since his return from the Soviet Union the year before and only the promise of the NASA work had been keeping him going these past months. Even his saving the life of the President would go unnoticed, his sacrifice unrewarded, his personal renunciation unheeded.

A symbol of their moving apart, the Oswald's sat on the lawn in silence, their shadows lengthening in the sunset, slowly moving toward the white picket fence, stopping at the threshold of it. The crickets began to hum.

Oswald felt totally isolated, alone. His entire world had collapsed on top of him, felling him, crushing him. With no one listening to his cries for help. No one to save him from the mad dogs.

'I guess I figured it would be best all round if I kept away,' was all he could say.

*

'Did you bring a sack or container with you to work the next day,' Kelley began wandering again, stroking his chin, 'I'm talking about Friday.'

'Yes, I did,' Lee recalled finding the cheese in the refrigerator and smiled inwardly as he remembered it was Ruth's favorite. He imagined her temper rising as she discovered half of it missing after he'd left for work.

'It was a paper bag and it contained my lunch and the curtain rods I spoke of.'

'What was the size or the shape of this bag?'

'I don't recall,' he shrugged, truthfully. 'I can't remember, you don't always find a sack that fits your sandwiches.'

'Lee, where did you put this sack, when you got in Frazier's car?'

Oswald looked down at Fritz, 'On my lap, or maybe at the side of me. I don't recall.'

'Could you have put it in the back seat of the car?' said Holmes.

'No, sir.'

'Well, Mister Frazier said you put a long package in the rear of his car that morning.'

'A long package? I don't know how long a long package is. It had curtain rods in it. He must be mistaken, or maybe thinking of some other time when he gave me a lift,' Oswald nodded.

Kelley leant against the door. The other officers remained silent and just stared at Oswald. He ignored them.

...stare all day...

'Would you describe Mister Frazier as a close friend?' continued Kelley, working around to something.

'I wouldn't, no,' Lee said, matter of factly.

'As just a friend?'

Lee thought a moment, as he pictured Wes Frazier, the gaunt, thin, teenager that he shared a drive with. In all their rides together, Oswald didn't recall much conversation between them and if there were any, it was Lee who would talk about his children.

'Mm, more of an acquaintance than a friend.'

'Do you think he'd lie, to get you in trouble?'

'No, I don't think he would, no. I hope not.'

Captain Fritz again redirected the questioning, 'What were your whereabouts and actions up to and at the time of the shooting.'

'The whole morning?' said Lee, surprised.

'If you want.'

*

'Wes, Lee's here for you.'

Linnie Mae Randle smiled at Lee as he poked his head through her open kitchen window. Oswald looked at her and returned the smile as he walked to the back door, walked through it and stepped into the kitchen. He saw the clock on the worktop: 7.15.

'Sit down, Lee, he won't be long.'

'Thanks.'

Lee sat down at the kitchen table and looked around. The house was almost the same design as Ruth's. Compact, to put it nicely.

'You want coffee?' Linnie turned from her dish washing to the steaming jug.

'Uh, no thanks, Mrs Randle. I'm just fine, thanks.'

Linnie moved back to her chores, 'How are you finding the work at the BookStore? Okay?'

'It's okay. By the way, I didn't get to thank you for telling Mrs. Paine about the opening. I really appreciated it, thanks.'

'That's okay, Lee. Anyway, it was rather selfish of me really. I just wanted you around so I could see that darlin' little baby girl of yours.'

Oswald smiled. 'Linnie,' he said, 'I happen to have two darlin' little baby girls ... in case you'd forgotten!'

'Oh, yes!' Linnie Mae blushed and returned to her sink. Lee looked around the kitchen drumming his fingers on the table.

'I think I'll be moving on though, I-'

Linnie May was startled as she turned to face him again, 'Moving on? When?'

'Oh, not for awhile, I guess. I was going to say, I'm trained in photography and the like, so ... without sounding snobbish or anything, uh, I'll be looking for work in that area.'

'Oh. Did you learn photographs in the army?'

'Marines,' Lee nodded.

'Oh,' Linnie returned to her lather covered plates. 'Will you be watching the President go by today, Lee? I understand from Wes that he's goin' right by the bookstore.'

'Uh, yes. Of course.'

'I wish I could be there,' she said, wistfully, 'but my mom called and she needs me this afternoon.'

'Couldn't you watch the motorcade, then go to your mothers?

'No, not really. Wes will have the car and be at work and all. I can catch the President on the TV.' Mrs. Randle looked up from the sink and gazed at a point somehwere out in the sky and said affectionately, 'You know, John Kennedy really is handsome. Don't you think?'

'Marina thinks so. She never misses him if he's on the television. I guess she'll be glued this afternoon.'

'Hi, Lee,' said Wes, coming through the doorway from the lounge, tucking in his shirt, 'be there in a minute.'

Oswald turned to see Wes crouched down, tying his shoelaces.

...big feet ...

'Lee was telling me that he might be moving on, Wes.'

Oswald groaned inwardly

... me and my big ...

'Not for a while though,' he added, quickly.

Wes looked at his sister, said, 'Linnie, Lee just got his job here! Don't you be going around tellin' nobody about what he said, now,' Wes bent over to tie the other lace. Oswald nodded at Wes.

Linnie, clearly hurt, said, 'Wesley Frazier, why would I do a thing like that? I only told you what he said.'

Wes stood. All six-five of him.

... Jee-sus, he's a giant! ... and only nineteen ...

'Okay, okay, Linnie. Look, I won't be late tonight. It's Friday, so there won't be any overtime. I'll see you around five-thirty.'

Wes went behind Linnie, put his long, thin arms around her and kissed her on the head.

'I'll take you to a movie tonight. You want to go the the movies tonight?'

Linnie half turned, smiling. 'Yeah, okay. That would be good.'

'Okay, Lee,' Wes picked up his jacket, draped over the back of the kitchen chair, 'let's go earn some corn.'

*

The gaunt, seven-storey building stood against the Dallas skyline. Its red bricks contrasting sharply with the blue skies above and behind it. For Lee, it had a foreboding air about it, a menacing nature. Wes drove across the turnpike and headed toward the underpass and Commerce Street. To say Lee had been quiet that morning would have been the understatement of the century. His belly had been in a knot since he woke, a curious churning in his stomach, matched only by the fire of indigestion burning through him.

The day was cool and rain had been forecast that morning.

If it rains, the President will have the bubbletop on his car ... Is it bullet proof? But surely, there won't be anybody shooting. Will there ... ?

'What's in the package, Lee?'

Oswald didn't hear Wes talking to him. The car sped on under the triple underpass, its sudden coolness sending a chill down his back. Lee thought of death.

... was it all blackness, like going into the shade of the underpass ... or was it nothing that any mortal could imagine ...probably ... I guess we all find out ...

'Lee?'

Oswald turned sharply to his left and looked at Wes. The driver thumbed the air behind him. 'What you got in the back?'

'Oh, just curtain rods. My apartment has no curtains and the landlady doesn't seem to understand English when I ask for something that might cost her money, so I got my own. Then I saw that there were no rods either.'

Wes laughed. 'Jeez, what time do you wake up in the mornings? I mean, you must be awake at dawn with the sun shinin' in and all.'

Oswald smiled, weakly. 'Tell me about it.'

Then they were out into the sunlight again.

'You think it's gonna rain?' said Oswald peering out of the door window, up at the heavens.

'Nah,' replied Wes, slowing the car as it reached the top of Commerce. 'Not today. Anyway, the President's in town around lunchtime! Hell, I hope it don't rain! I don't wanna miss the parade.'

'Yeah. Me neither.'

Wes turned left onto Houston Street, the traffic busy in the morning rush. 'How's your drivin' goin', Lee? Linnie told me Mrs. Paine is takin' you out.'

'That's right. I've been out a couple of times. Getting the hang of it, I guess.'

'Well, it's a good thing to be able to do. Opens up new job prospects and all that kind of thing. Best thing is though, is that you can just up and fly whenever you feel like it.'

... like now, off to New Orleans ...

'Since I started livin' with my sister, I never did have so much money, you know what I mean? Sure, I help her out with the house keepin' an' groceries an' all, but I have money over. I can spend it on whatever I like, when I like.'

'Well,' said Lee, 'you keep on enjoying every minute of it, Wes, 'cos when you have a wife and two kids, you ain't going to have any money, no matter how much you earn.' Oswald spoke bitterly. Wes glanced at him and figured that any more talk along this line was definitely a no-no.

The car crossed Elm Street and passed between the BookStore on the left and the Dal-Tex building on the right. Again, the car passed through cool shadow, before turning left behind the Book Depository building and into the car park. Wes had his own special spot for parking and was glad to see that no one had taken it. As they passed the loading bay Wes spoke again.

'Give me a shout when you're fixing for lunch.'

Oswald grunted and got out of the car. Turning back, he reached over the seat to pick up his package. Wes got out and locked the driver's door. Package cupped under his shoulder, Lee walked off toward the loading bay ramp.

'Wait up, Lee ...' said Wes, locking the passenger door. Lee didn't hear him.

Oswald was a good fifty feet in front of Wes when he

reached the ramp. Lee climbed the stairs and walked into the shadow of the loading bay area. Passing the elevators to his left, Lee walked into the BookStore warehouse area through the high loading bay doors, turned sharply left and headed for the Domino room, located in the corner of the building.

'Mornin', Lee,' Lee's foreman, Bill Shelley greeted Oswald as he passed the toilets.

'Morning,' Oswald replied and walked into the Domino room. Shelley was behind him and stuck his head around the door as Lee put the package onto one of the tables and sat down.

'I need you on the sixth floor this morning, Lee. Harold will be getting down the Rolling Reader's order for Ferguson.'

Oswald looked at him. 'What's going on up there today, Bill?'

'I want you to help the floor laying crew finish up.'

'They not done yet? Jeez, I could do work like that for the money they get.'

'Don't let it bother you too much. Most of those guys will be laid off after this job.'

'Yeah, I guess there's always that.'

'Trouble is when you get into a job like that, casual labor, you get laid off all the time. You don't pay no dues or nothin', so you ain't got a leg to stand on. People treat you like chicken shit.'

'And people don't anyway?' Oswald said, gloomily.

'See you later,' said Shelley, turning and moving back into the storage area. Oswald nodded and looked at his curtain rods.

... what a fucking excuse to see your wife and kids ... I won't be needing these things where I'm going ...

Oswald placed the package behind one of the chairs and went to the elevator to the sixth floor.

*

The morning passed and Lee became increasingly depressed. Working with the floor laying crew didn't help. Bill Shelley's 'casuals' were living up to their name. The whole of the floor's central area had been re-timbered and Lee and the casuals were taking the cut down old planks of wood down to the loading area in the elevator.

Lee had no conversation for these men, talking about drinking and women in a way that Lee despised. He was no feminist, but women shouldn't be talked about in that way. He ignored them and it didn't take them long to make him the butt of their jokes, whether, he figured, he could hear them or not.

'You watchin' the parade, Lee?'

Oswald looked up from his work and wiped the sweat from his brow. One of the regular employees stood over him.

'Sure, Jimmy, I'll try and get as much of this done before the President comes by,' Lee glanced sideways at some of the floor laying crew, then back at Jimmy. 'If I leave it to these guys, I'll be workin' Christmas Day."

'Okay, see you later,' Jimmy turned and began to walk away.

'Jim,' shouted Oswald, 'what time is it?'

Jimmy stopped and looked at his watch. 'Just about eleven-forty-five. I'm going down now, Kennedy's here sometime after twelve.'

Oswald watched his colleague go to the elevator. The floor laying crew had heard Oswald's conversation and began to move to the elevators. Oswald watched them go and then walked down to the fifth floor via the north west stair well. He began checking off some late deliveries, but his mind was elsewhere.

... still no news from Bishop or anyone ... Ruby didn't call ... I'll have to go to the theater later ... as Ferrie told me ... damn ...why

no contact with Bishop ... and what kind of reception am I going to get from Ruby and Ferrie when their plan doesn't come off ... where are those guys with the rifles? ... what the hell is going down? ...

...I'll need to get to New Orleans fast to pick up my money ... there's a thought, will we all get paid for this failed attempt ... or will we be moved to the next point, the next place to pull of their crazy stunt... would Ruby and the others be picked up by the FBI...?

Oswald sighed heavily and threw down his clipboard. Putting his hands on his hips he looked around the dirty warehouse.

... can this be the sum of my life ... is this it?

Lee's mind went blank and he held his head low, touching his chest with his chin. Picking up his clipboard, he moved to the elevator. Remembering that all the boys had just gone down on them he ran up the stair well, back to the sixth floor. Ahead of him were hundreds and hundreds of cardboard boxes, all full of children's books. All of the floor, save the central area, was a maze of these stacks of cartons, obscuring the southern windows overlooking the Plaza.

Lee listened and thought he heard a whisper in the cool, dark atmosphere of the warehouse. Turning his head this way and that he concluded he'd been mistaken. From a nearby open window, Lee could hear the growing anticipation of the gathering crowd outside. He moved into the central area and looked around.

He looked down at the clipboard again.

... why the hell am I bothering to fill this damn thing ...what's the point of this whole sham ... Bishop's not gonna call ... there ... I finally let the damn thought in ... something is wrong here ... Something is definitely not right ...

A voice startled him, a voice that came from the elevator behind him.

'Boy, are you going downstairs? It's near lunchtime.'

Lee looked and saw one of his workmates. 'No, sir, not yet. When you get downstairs, close the gate to the elevator so I can use it. Would you do that for me?'

'Okay.'

The elevator dropped from Oswald's sight. Again, Lee thought he heard something behind him, a voice or movement and he wandered back into the central area of the floor.

... somebody around here? Who the hell would be up here at a time like this ...

Lee heard the elevator hit the ground, the door slide and the movement of his colleague stepping out. Straining, he hoped to hear the sliding of the metal mesh gate be moved back into position, so the elevator would answer his signal and return to the sixth floor.

He heard nothing.

... Goddammit ...

Oswald moved to the elevator shaft and held the closed gate. Looking down into the shaft, Lee could just get an angle on what would be the roof of the elevator. He pulled and pushed the gate, making a racket, shouting down the shaft.

'Hey! Hey!' Lee's voice echoed into the shaft but was lost in the blackness. 'Close the gate! Are you there? Close the gate ...'

... dammit ...

Oswald kicked the gate and listened angrily while it rattled itself into silence. 'How about an elevator, guys?'

Again, there was no reply and again he kicked the gate.

... Jeez... now I'll have to walk down ...

Lee moved to the stairwell and, clipboard in hand, walked down the dark and dismal steps. All the way down he kept wondering about the lack of communication from Bishop, from anyone, that could keep him in the picture regarding the day's events.

... maybe I should split now ... that would mean the end of my cover, one way or another ... even if they did get the President, they'd

still be after me … no, I'll just have to sweat it out … not long to go now … then we'll just see how the land lies …

Lee wondered if his dizziness were the effects of his depression or the continual winding of his journey down the stairwell. He chose the latter, tried vainly to put some kind of spark into his soul and promised himself some kind of personal reward for all his efforts. Passing no-one on the stairwell did not surprise him. He rightly guessed that everyone would either be eating lunch or out on the streets of the Plaza vying to get a good view of the passing motorcade, or both. As he descended, heading for the Domino room on the ground floor of the eastern end of the BookStore, Oswald slowed his steps in an effort to prolong his journey.

He didn't want the steps to end.

Lee sat down in the Domino room, chewing on his cheese sandwich. He noticed the curtain rods, still lying behind one of the chairs, where he'd left them earlier. The clipboard and papers littered the table.

… damn landlady … how about renting a room with no damn curtains … should be a law against it …

Outside, Lee could hear the crowds laughing and the general chatter of conversations about the President and just about everything else. He chewed his last sandwich very slowly and took a final gulp of his Coke. Finishing that, Lee stood and walked to the wastebin in the corner of the room and threw the empty bottle into it. Returning to his lunch, he pushed the remaining bread and cheese into his mouth and threw the wrapping paper into the bin also.

He began to pace up and down the room. At that point several of his work colleagues came in to eat lunch. He turned away from them and moved to the door and left.

The President was scheduled to pass in front of the building at approximately twelve-thirty, but Lee figured it would be later than that in view of the crowds and such, plus Kennedy's continual headache for the Secret Service: getting out of the vehicle and walking amongst the crowd, pumping hands and chatting.

Lee turned a sharp left and headed for the main doorway entrance, facing the Plaza. As he passed Bill Shelley's office and then Superintendent Roy Truly's, Oswald noticed that neither of them were there, that they must be outside.

The approach to the main entrance was a strange one for Lee. Of course, he'd walked this way a hundred times since he began work here barely a month ago, but today was different. Today he knew he was walking it for the last time, that whatever happened in the next few minutes outside in the November sunshine, he would never again walk in this building.

*

As he spoke, Oswald kept his eyes on Kelley, now staring out of the window of the office. Lee tried to follow his line of vision, but could not.

'I saw the President shot, or rather, I was stood in the doorway with some of the guys, in back of them, then there was all the commotion and I went back inside and got a Coke from the machine on the second floor.'

'Was that when the policeman stopped you?' Continued Fritz, ticking off his questions on the note pad.

'Yes, though that was a little later,' again, Oswald tried to see what Kelley could be looking at. He gave up.

'How much later?' Fritz raised his voice in an effort to regain Oswald's full attention.

'Oh, a couple of minutes or so, I guess. I'd just gotten a bottle of Coke and was drinking it, when this cop bursts in and shoves his pistol in my belly. Mister Truly, the manager said "he works here" or something like that and then they ran out. I left the building then.'

'How did you get to the second floor? What route did you take?'

Oswald looked at Fritz and, clasping his hands, leant forward onto the two front legs of his chair.

'Let me see ... the motorcade had just passed and everybody was running around and shouting and so on. I went back into the building through the main entrance and turned right and went up the stairs.'

'How far from these stairs is the lunchroom where you bought your drink?'

'Well, it's on the other side of the building, the north side of the building.'

'How far?'

'About... I don't know how far, but you would have to go past some offices, it's not a direct route. There's a counter in an open space, a couple of doors and so on.'

'In terms of time, how long did it take you to get to the lunchroom?'

'Not long. A minute or maybe two.'

Inspector Holmes spoke: 'Lee, do you know anybody or have you heard of anybody answering to the name of Alex James Hidell?'

... again ...

'No. I've told you all about that,' Lee sat back into his chair, tight lipped.

'Have you ever used that name as an alias?'

...relentless ...

'No, I haven't. I have never used that name, I don't know anybody by that name and I've never heard the name before you people mentioned it to me.'

Fritz paused. Oswald knew what was going to follow.

'Well, what about the Hidell I.D. card we found in your wallet, Friday?'

... bingo ...

'I've told you all I'm going to tell you about that card,' Lee sat forward and gaped at the police captain. 'You took notes, just read them for yourself, if you want to refresh your memory.' Lee jabbed a finger at the Captain, saying firmly. 'You have the card. Now you know as much about it as I do.'

'I'm through,' said Fritz, ignoring Oswald's stare as he rubbed his eyeglasses with a handkerchief. 'Gus, how are we on the transfer?'

'No word yet, but I'm sure we're pretty close. I'll check it out.'

Gus Rose left the office. Oswald watched him leave then turned his head to the Captain.

'Where are you taking me?' demanded Oswald.

The Captain replaced his spectacles, his eyes suddenly larger beneath the thick glass. 'County Jail, Lee. We can't keep you here indefinitely. That way, it's safer all round. For you, me, everyone.'

As Fritz spoke, Chief Curry and two of his men appeared at the door. Curry knocked on the glass and Fritz motioned him to come in. Curry stood in the doorway and addressed the Captain. Oswald looked past the Chief at the tallest of the officers who had arrived with Curry. Lee estimated the man's height at just six feet and coming in at two hundred and twenty pounds, clean-shaven, fair face, bright, blue eyes and aged thirty-five.

The odd thing that struck Lee was the man's suit. Whereas, everybody else he'd seen over that weekend had been dressed in black or dark blue, this giant had on a white suit, white shirt and was complete with a white Stetson cowboy hat. The detective was looking over at Oswald whilst his superiors conversed.

'Will, are you ready for the man to be transferred?' Curry did not look at Oswald, who began to scrutinize the Police Chief.

Fritz stood and moved a couple of paces toward Curry. 'We're ready just as soon as the security is in place.'

'I have instructed that the television cameras be moved away from the doorway to the parking area, the people have been moved back, all the crews and such. They're well back in the garage,' replied the Chief.

'Then I think we're all ready to go.'

Curry half-turned to the man with him. 'Okay. Chief Stevenson and I will meet you at the County Jail.'

'Right.'

Curry and his colleague closed the door as they left.

The Captain stood, nodded to Kelley and began to talk to his detectives. Oswald looked at Kelley, who was approaching him.

... what now ... another type of interrogation ...

Tom Kelley pulled up his left trouser leg slightly and sat on the edge of the desk. Before engaging Oswald with his stare, Lee could see the man forming the question in his head. Kelley smoothed the folds in his trousers before allowing his eyes to lock onto Oswald's. Kelley spoke quietly, carefully framing his words. Oswald found himself listening intently to the Secret Service agent and looking deeply into Kelley's deep brown eyes, a hint of sadness behind them. The Secret Service man was obviously under a great deal of strain.

... but not as much as me ...

'Lee, as you can imagine, we're pretty anxious to speak with you regarding this matter,' Kelley paused as he carefully framed his sentences, his breathing was somewhat labored, as if he were desperate to speak to Oswald privately, 'and anything else that you may have to tell us. You know, of course that being the Secret Service, we were responsible for the security surrounding President Kennedy ...'

Kelley trailed off, looking to the floor. Oswald saw the first hint of emotion from anyone who'd been in charge of him that weekend and it made him feel good, none-the-less. Kelley came back from his own thoughts and continued, ' ... we're in trouble, I'll tell you that.'

'I did wonder about that,' Oswald found himself genuinely sympathetic.

'Well, yeah.'

Kelley pulled at his face with one of his free hands, as if he might tear the skin from his lined countenance. 'Now, as you know, the Dallas Police have charged you with the assassination of the President and the shooting of Officer Tippit-'

'Tell me,' interrupted Lee, 'which one are they most sore about? The President or this Tippit guy?'

Kelley half-smiled and looked Lee in the eye. 'Well, without me maligning someone, I think you know the answer to that. Anyway, when you have secured counsel, we need to talk. We're very anxious that the correct story develops and I know that you are.'

'That, of course, is an understatement.' Oswald scratched his head, his manacles rattling as he did so. 'Sure, I'd be happy to talk with you. Whatever my counsel tells me, I'll do. I have nothing to hide, I did not shoot anyone. I haven't done anything wrong. I just need to get out of this place to prove it, that's all,' Oswald tossed his head back, rolling his eyes across the walls and ceiling.

Kelley followed Lee's dialogue to the letter. 'Yes, that's all. I see your point. Well, you'll be on your way in a matter of minutes now. Is there anything you want to tell me now, before you go?'

Like what Kelley... like the fact that I know the details of this entire scam ... that I personally know at least two of the individuals involved ...like I work for the Bureau as an informant ... you want my cash number? S172... have you bothered to enquire about the voucher in my pocket that's worth two hundred dollars ... or didn't they tell you about that ...

Lee looked at the agent. 'Not really. I don't think I should speak about it anymore. We'll see when I get me a lawyer.'

The door burst open. Oswald, Kelley, Fritz and the other officers in the room spun their heads to see who had disturbed them. A uniform stood at the door, holding some items of clothing. As he entered and put the garments onto the desk, he said, to no one in particular. 'Chief says you may need these, Captain.' With that, the uniform spun on his heel and left.

Fritz passed a dark blue long-sleeved shirt to Lee. 'You want to put this on? It's a little chilly out there.'

Oswald stood and pointed to a white shirt next to a black sweater, 'I'd rather wear those, if I may, sir.'

Kelley passed the shirt and sweater to Oswald. The Captain produced the keys to Lee's handcuffs and slipped the left cuff.

'Thanks,' said Oswald, picking up the shirt and pulling it on.

The Captain spoke as Oswald was buttoning up his shirt. 'You want a hat or something? You know, to hide yourself or anything? Everybody out there has seen you bareheaded ...'

'No, thank you, Captain. I don't need anything like that. I've done nothing to be ashamed of.'

He pulled the sweater over and up his left arm and over his head. Sweater donned, Lee held up his wrists. That done, Fritz replaced the cuffs.

Fritz turned to the white suit. 'Leavelle, you want to get with this guy?'

The detective moved past his colleagues to confront the prisoner. Oswald didn't take his eyes off Leavelle as he approached. Fritz's telephone rang and Kelley answered it.

'Captain?' Fritz turned to see Kelley holding out the receiver to him. 'Chief Curry.'

Fritz took the phone. 'Fritz,' he said, watching Leavelle move toward the prisoner. '...what? well, no, Jess, I certainly don't agree with that... because a car would give us more speed should anything happen... an armored truck for Christ's sakes...'

'You wanna get up, Oswald?' said Leavelle, producing another set of handcuffs from his trouser pocket. Oswald stood, but was busy looking over the giant detective's shoulder, listening to Fritz on the phone.

'Okay,' said the man in the white suit, 'for your own protection, I'm gonna cuff you to myself for the whole journey to the County jail. Where I go, you go. Where you go, I go.'

Oswald ignored him.

Fritz continued. 'I suggest we use an unmarked car or similar, driven by one of our people… yes, for maneuverability and speed… yes.'

Fritz surveyed the office and caught Oswald listening to him. The police captain held Lee's gaze. Leavelle tapped Lee on the arm. Oswald looked down and held out his right hand. Leavelle produced his black handcuffs. Placing one cuff onto his own left hand, the detective snapped the other onto Oswald's right wrist.

Leavelle looked into Oswald's eyes. 'I sure hope if anyone shoots at you that they're as good a shot as you are.'

Lee sniggered. 'Don't worry. No-one is going to shoot at me.'

'… the armored truck could leave first, followed by another car with only officers in it, then the unmarked car containing the prisoner… yes, then, after one or maybe two blocks, the car with Oswald in it will turn off and go directly to the County Jail. The armored car and the other vehicle would take the previously agreed route…'

Fritz paused a while as Curry spoke to him, then he replaced the receiver. 'That's it, let's go,' he said, picking up and donning his Stetson, moving to the office door.

I must get me one of those …

The prisoner and his captors moved into the Homicide Area. No newspaper reporters were in the corridor and Lee could see that the door was wide open, two detectives stood either side of it. Fritz stopped next to them, saying, 'Chris, I want you and Charlie to go down to the basement garage. Move the follow up car and the transfer car into place on the auto ramp, Commerce Street side. I understand from Chief

Curry that the armored car is in position.'

'Yes, sir, that's correct,' said Detective Brown.

'Okay,' The Captain turned on his heels to his left to face another of his men. 'Pierce?' he said, 'Go to the car pool and get another car to act as a lead car.'

'Yes, sir,' said Pierce and left the office.

'How are we down there, Baker?' Fritz said to the detective to Oswald's right front. Baker held a telephone receiver to his ear.

'They're all fine down in the basement, Captain,' said Baker, 'I've notified them that the prisoner is on his way down.'

'Okay, thank you.' Fritz turned to his men, 'Let's go then.'

The small group of men moved into the strangely empty corridor, the same walkway Lee had been pushed and pulled up and down may times since his arrest, two days previously. It seemed odd to him to be leaving the police station in this less than dramatic way, that the press wouldn't witness his move to the County Jail. He began to think of Bishop and couldn't help wondering if this were part of the plan to get him out of the hands of the police, to get him away where he might be safe from the people he'd met and worked with that previous summer in New Orleans...

...has Bishop got me out of this... too bad I couldn't get to Bookhout or Hosty... still, I'm out of here soon, then I can get me a lawyer and go about blowing the lid off this thing...

They passed a water fountain built into the wall and moved into the lobby where the jail elevator was located. A grim faced uniform was guarding the entrance to the elevator. Seeing the captain and the prisoner, the policeman stepped aside. Lee walked with Leavelle, feeling dwarfed by the big man, hardly matching his stride. Leavelle had put his left hand half into Lee's pant's pocket, keeping a firm grip on him.

No-body spoke and the silence became almost overwhelming.

On entering the elevator, the uniform slammed the gate shut and the captain slid the inner door to. Lee stood at the rear of it, Leavelle to his right and another detective to his left. With two other detectives crammed like sardines in the slight elevator, the Captain threw the lever and the hoist dropped.

It was dark in the small, rattling, elevator as it dropped swiftly to its destination, the very bowels of the Police Department Building. If anything needed painting in this God forsaken place, the elevator did. Dirty fingerprints surrounded the elevator motor handle, several palm prints daubed the walls. Oswald eyed his captors, optics dancing from right to left.

Someone's cologne drifted sweetly in the stale air, Lee's nostrils flared as he caught the fragrance.

All seemed well.

Oswald let his thoughts slip to Marina and the kids.

...where are they?

Lee wondered, feeling a little anxious for their safety.

...where the hell have the cops taken them?

Lee peered ahead at the Captain's rounded shoulders.

... must be coming up to retirement ...seems like a good idea ...

Fritz spoke, abruptly. 'Gonna be a lot of press down here, Lee.'

The Captain half-turned toward Oswald, dim electric light from the tiny bulb catching his eyeglasses. 'Don't worry about it. It's all under control. They'll throw a couple of dozen questions at a time at you-'

'Tell me about it.'

'-But don't let that bother you none. We'll be at the County Jail in no time.'

The elevator reached the basement with a crash, slightly jarring tense bones. The hoist rocked as it steadied itself.

Fritz said, 'Here we go,' and pulled back the doors.

Fritz, Oswald, Leavelle and the other detectives who had ridden down to the basement walked slowly into the basement jail area.

Directly ahead, Lee saw a television crew filming him as he turned left past the jail office, a uniform straining himself to get a better look at the history passing before him. Oswald could hear voices, though he didn't know if they were police or reporters.

'Here he is,' said one voice to his front. Simultaneously, the same words were spoken from a different location.

Fritz took the lead, as they passed through a narrow aisle to the front of the office. Fritz walked backwards for a few steps, then stopped and turned.

'Jim, you get with Oswald.'

Another detective moved to Oswald, taking hold of Lee's left upper arm. He felt the strength in the detective's hand as he gripped him tightly. Now he was totally shackled between the two police officers, not that escape crossed his mind. He realized that that would be a futile gesture, one that would possibly result in a somewhat unpleasant ending for him.

'Here he comes …' Lee heard someone say again, as the entourage moved past the jail office, led by Captain Fritz. Several spotlights burst into life, illuminating them, the low din through the doors increased in volume.

… camera lights… television…

'The car is in position,' said an officer to Fritz. He nodded, as two cameramen ran in front of them, out into the basement area, carrying cables and equipment. Oswald moved his head slightly, to keep them in view, but he didn't see them after they passed through the doors ahead. Lee could now hear the sounds of a crowd, not unlike a big game about to start and his heart sank a little. He thought he'd be somewhat used to it by now, but the fear of the exposure lingered and a chill ran down his spine.

One of the detectives went through the door into the basement and they all followed. As they passed through the door, Leavelle stopped. Oswald and the other detective holding Lee's arm almost walked into him.

Oswald saw a group of news reporters and cameramen to his right, stood just in front of some double swinging doors that led back into the jail area. The commotion increased, Lee could see people darting around in the basement gloom, ghostly shadows behind the arc lights beating down on him. Leavelle looked through the doors. Oswald could see the police car backing up into position.

... *didn't someone say that car was ready?*

Leavelle began to walk forward, pulling Oswald's pants as he did so. A car horn echoed through the basement, a sharp startling sound drowning the commotion for the briefest time.

'Here he is!' Somebody hollered from the crowd.

Lee was compelled to follow Leavelle. Moving slightly faster than the white suited detective, Lee got into stride with the big Texan, the detective at his left moved with them. Captain Fritz walked on, a little further in front of the trio and a considerable gap appeared between them.

Lee felt the presence of the other detective bringing up the rear. Already, he caught the sounds of questions being shouted at him but didn't even consider stopping and answering them. Lee was almost out and didn't need any more distractions.

Captain Fritz was almost at the car, which was still backing into position.

Oswald and the two detectives were only a few feet behind, moving briskly. More arc lights, combined with popping camera bulbs, continued to dazzle all of them. Lee fixed his gaze on the car in front and saw the red tail-lights come on as the driver applied the brakes. Newsmen to Oswald's rear, those from the double doors, moved after him. He could hear them cursing as he left them, their equipment slowing their movements.

In the shadows to Lee's left, stood about fifty newsmen.

Some held microphones, some held cameras as he approached them. Many police officers stood amongst the crowd, holding the multitude back. Had they not been there, Oswald and those in charge of him would have been engulfed, swamped.

Lee looked at them as he walked with Leavelle and his colleague, eyes adjusting to the flashes of light. By now, Lee was seeing tracers, as his eyelids would twitch and squint, randomly focusing on any flashbulb.

More and more questions were shouted at him and he felt vulnerable, exposed and more than a little fearful.

As he moved to the slowing vehicle, Lee's heart sank, his mouth turning dry in an instant.

There, in among the news reporters, standing menacingly was Jack Ruby, hands down by his sides, lurking in the darkness of the basement. Lee saw Ruby's dark Fedora, recognized his long nose, the sunken eyes beneath the brim lost in the roundness of his chubby face, staring at him.

... staring ...

More light bulbs flashed, more questions flew through the air at him. Confusion set into Oswald's mind, his senses tingling, stinging.

... Ruby ... what is he ... sonofa ... here?

A microphone suddenly appeared under Lee's nose, a reporter with a white overcoat, standing next to Ruby, moved forward two steps and shouted.

'Do you have anything to say?'

Lee ignored him, turning away, moving toward the car ... the momentum from his captors meant Oswald had to go with them.

Out of the corner of his eye and as he heard the car horn shatter the air for the second time, Lee thought he saw someone close to Ruby lunge forward...

Aftermath

Lee Harvey Oswald died at 1.13pm in Parkland Memorial Hospital on 24 November 1963, just less than 48 hours after President John F Kennedy had been pronounced dead at the same venue. The single bullet fired by a supposedly grief stricken Jack Ruby into Oswald's abdomen caused severe injury to the alleged assassin's aorta, spleen, left lung, knocked out part of his main instestine, went through the abdominal main vein, the right kidney and completely through his liver. Despite these fatal injuries, the bullet did not exit his body and was found just beneath the skin on his right side. Doctor Charles Crenshaw and others operated on their patient for almost one and a half hours before Oswald succumbed to the assault. Oswald did not regain consciousness and gave no deathbed confession.

Following an autopsy, Oswald was buried the next day, at the same time as JFK, in Rose Hill Cemetery, Fort Worth, under the name of William Bobo, another Dallasite who had just died. The false name was used to protect Oswald's gravestone, but it was later stolen anyway. Oswald's wife, Marina, their two daughters, Oswald's mother Marguerite and elder brother Robert attended the service. Seven members of the attending reporters were pressed into service as pallbearers.

After his arrest (he was taken to the same cell that his victim had just vacated) Jack Ruby maintained that he had shot Oswald 'for Jackie and Caroline,' claiming that he didn't want the former First Lady to have to attend Oswald's trial. On 14 March 1964, Ruby was found guilty of the murder of Oswald at his own trial and he was sentenced to death by the electric chair. Rumours began almost immediately that Ruby had known Oswald and the latter had been a 'guest' at his Carousel Club only days before the assassination.

Beverley Oliver, one of Jack Ruby's girls, claims that Ruby introduced her to Oswald as 'Lee Oswald of the CIA.' The same rumour puts one David Ferrie sat with Oswald on the same evening and although this author has yet to see it, claims abound that a photograph exists showing the three men together at Ruby's night club. Considering Oswald's relationship with US intelligence, it was later revealed that Jack Ruby had been contacted 'by the FBI nine times in 1959... to furnish information'. This fact was covered up by the Warren Commission at the behest of J Edgar Hoover, then Director of the FBI.

Ruby was personally known to most of the Dallas Police in 1963 and was often seen at the police station. Whatever his relationship with the Dallas police, Ruby certainly had access to the building following Oswald's arrest on 22 November 1963 as revealed by news footage taken in the Dallas Police Building over that weekend. Ruby is seen in the background as Oswald is led from one office to another, even correcting Dallas DA Henry Wade when the official stated to newsmen that Oswald had been a member of the 'Free Cuba Committee'. Was Ruby stalking his prey before he shot him on that Sunday morning?

Upon appeal, Jack Ruby was granted a re-trial, set for 1967, but died before any hearings were held. Ruby told family members that he was convinced the authorities were trying to silence him by injecting cancer cells into his body. This has never been proved. Two months before Ruby's death on 3 January 1967, Jim Garrison, then district Attorney of New Orleans Parish, announced that his office was to investigate the murder of John Kennedy, after he discovered that Lee Harvey Oswald had lived in New Orleans the summer of 1963, and had been in contact, one way or another, with individuals connected to the US Intelligence system. Ruby was the first of the 'principal' witnesses to die after Garrison announced his intention to bring the killers of John Kennedy to justice. David Ferrie followed Ruby a month later, again under suspicious circumstances. Before the deaths of Ruby and Ferrie, a 1966 article by the *London Sunday Times* quoted the odds were 100,000 trillion to one that so many witnesses would die, violently or otherwise, so soon after the assassination.

As early as two weeks after the murder of President Kennedy, polls showed that no less than 52% of the American public did not believe Oswald could have carried out the assassination alone. Since then, the number has grown to well over 90%, with a great number asking if Oswald had any part in the assassination at all. In 1979, the House Select Committe on Assassinations concluded that a shot had been fired from the front right of the President, from the area known as the 'grassy knoll' - this, of course, meant conspiracy. In fact, a revolver similar to that taken from Oswald in the theater at the time of his arrest, was found in a brown paper bag 'in the general area of where the assassination of President Kennedy took place' as described in a suppressed memo by the FBI for thirty years. The results of the investigation pertaining to the weapon found have not yet been released.

Since the HSCA closed its investigation concluding President Kennedy 'was probably assassinated as a result of a conspiracy', nothing has happened. No further investigations, no arrests. Nothing. Since that dark day in Dallas forty years ago, many have been implicated in the assassination of John Kennedy, but only one person has been brought to trial - Clay Shaw - and he was aquitted in 1969.

Robert F Kennedy, the president's younger brother and Attorney General at the time of the assassination, believed that most of the questions relating to his brother's murder, went unanswered. He told friends that, 'subject to being elected president, I would like to re-open the Warren Commission.' Some have questioned why Robert F Kennedy, at the time the head of the United States Justice Department, did not head up an investigation into his brother's death. We will never know the reasons for that, for Robert F Kennedy was himself cut down by an assassin's bullet in June 1968, just after he had won the Californian Primary and was clearly heading for the White House that Fall.

Even Chief Justice Earl Warren, the man who had lent his name to the President's Commission into the Assassination of President Kennedy, told the American public following the publication of the Warren Report that, 'we will never know the whole truth about the assassination.' The list goes on, and includes others who were at the front of the investigation, such as Dallas Police Chief Jesse Curry. Curry always believed that two assassins were involved. He said, 'We don't have any proof that Oswald fired that rifle. No one has ever put him in that building with a gun in his hand.'

What did Oswald tell Curry in the two days of his incarceration? We are told that no notes were kept and that no tape recordings were made of Oswald's interrogation. As late as 1977, Dallas District Attorney Henry Wade told author and photographic expert Robert Groden that, 'I never did believe that Oswald acted alone.' Even Presidential aide Kenny O'Donnell, riding in a car just behind JFK, stated that he heard at least one shot from the front right of Kennedy's limousine (the infamous grassy knoll) and that he thought there had been a conspiracy. John McCone, then CIA Director and Warren Commission member, told Robert Kennedy that he believed there had been two gunmen involved in the shooting.

Aftermath

*

The following list shows the number of people connected to the case who have died, in mysterious circumstances or otherwise, since 22 November 1963.

(* Indicates suspicious death).

November 1963

President John F Kennedy*

Dallas Police Officer J D Tippit*

Lee Harvey Oswald*

Karyn Kupcinet*

TV host's daughter who was overheard telling of JFK's death prior to the event, was found murdered two days after the assassination. Her father was an aquaintance of Jack Ruby.

The Warren Commission Investigation 1964

December 1963

Jack Zangretti*

Expressed foreknowledge of Jack Ruby shooting Oswald. Zangretti died of a gunshot wound.

February 1964

Eddy Benavides*

Domingo Benavides, sat in his parked truck eating lunch, witnessed the Tippit murder from less than twenty yards away and was the nearest witness to the shooting, having a clear view of Tippit and his killer. Only hours later Benavides failed to identify Oswald as the killer of Tippit. He then began to receive death threats and later Domingo's look-a-like brother Eddy was murdered after a fight broke out in a bar, in which he received a fatal gunshot to the head. Domingo not surprisingly changed his story and said that Tippit's killer resembled Oswald.

Betty MacDonald*

Warren Reynolds saw a man rushing away from the scene of the Tippit murder and followed him for a block before the assailant dis-

appeared from his sight. Hours later, at the Dallas Police Department, he would not identify the man as Lee Oswald. In January 1964, Reynolds, whilst in the basement of the used car lot where he worked, was shot in the head at almost point blank range. He was not robbed of money or possessions. Miraculously, he survived and not surprisingly changed his story, identifying Oswald as Tippit's killer. A man named Darrell Wayne Garner was then arrested for shooting Reynolds. Betty MacDonald, who had worked for Jack Ruby, gave Garner an alibi. She was later arrested for fighting with her roommate (who wasn't arrested) and found hanged in her police cell. Her death was ruled suicide.

March 1964

Bill Chesher

Thought to have information linking Oswald and Ruby, died of a heart attack.

Hank Killam*

Husband of Ruby stripper Wanda Joyce Killam, friend of Oswald acquaintance John Carter, who shared a rooming house with Oswald and dated one of Ruby's strippers. Killam told his brother, 'I am a dead man, but I have run as far as I am going to run.' Found with his throat cut in Pensacola, Florida. Police said the death was probably accidental, newspapers stated that he had either fallen or jumped through a plate glass window.

April 1964

Bill Hunter*

A Californian newspaper reporter who was in Ruby's apartment with Ruby's roommate George Senator and **Dallas Times Herald** *reporter Jim Koethe on the evening of the murder of Oswald. Ruby was by then in police custody. Hunter died in an accidental shooting by a police officer in Long Beach, California police station basement.*

May 1964

Gary Underhill*

One time CIA contract agent who told friends that the Agency was involved in the JFK assassination and that he feared for his life.

Died of a gunshot wound to the left side of his head. Though Underhill was right handed, his death was ruled a suicide.

Hugh Ward*

Private investigator who was working with Guy Banister and David Ferrie. Ward died when the plane he was piloting crashed in Mexico.

DeLesseps Morrison*

Morrison was a New Orleans mayor and a passenger in Hugh Ward's plane that fateful trip.

June 1964

W Guy Banister*

Former Chicago FBI agent who ran anti-Castro factions in New Orleans and was connected to David Ferrie, CIA, ONI and New Orleans Mafia head Carols Marcello. Banister's secretary, Delphine Roberts, claimed that Lee Oswald used Banister's office during the summer of 1963 whilst Oswald was involved in the bogus Fair Play For Cuba Committee. When informed by Roberts that Oswald was outside giving out pro-Castro leaflets, Banister is reported to have said that she shouldn't worry and that "Oswald is one of ours." Died shortly before the Warren Commission was published and was never called to appear before that committee. His death was reported to be either a heart attack or a gunshot wound.

August 1964

Teresa Norton*

aka Karen Bennett Carlin, aka Little Lynn. Ruby employee and was the last known person to speak with Ruby before he gunned down Lee Oswald. Norton allegedly asked Ruby for money, giving him a reason to be at the bank near the police station at the time of Oswald's transfer. She is alleged to have died from a gunshot, yet no death certificate exists - it is not clear if she is dead or alive.

September 1964

Jim Koethe*

Newspaper reporter who was in Ruby's apartment on 24/11/63 with Bill Hunter and George Senator. Koethe died from a karate blow to the neck.

C.D. Jackson

Life magazine senior vice president who bought Abraham Zapruder's film of the assassination and kept it locked it away in the Time - Life vaults until 1975. It is not known how he died.

Maurice B Gatlin

Associate of Guy Banister, fell to his death from his hotel window in Panama City just before the Warren Commission was published.

October 1964

Mary Pinchot Meyer*

JFK mistress whose diary was confiscated by former CIA chief James Angleton after her murder.

January 1965

Paul Mandal

Life magazine writer who described JFK turning to rear to clear discrepancy of JFK's throat wound being an entry wound. The Zapruder film clearly shows that JFK did not turn around during the shooting. Mandal died from cancer.

Tom Howard*

Ruby's first lawyer, who was in Ruby's apartment on 24/11/63 after Ruby shot Oswald. Howard told Ruby to tell the police that he had shot Oswald in an effort to stop Jackie Kennedy attending Oswald's trial. He died from a heart attack.

August 1965

Mona B. Saenz*

Texas Employment clerk who interviewed Oswald about his job at the Book Depository. Hit by Dallas bus.

David Goldstein

Dallasite who helped FBI trace ownership of Oswald's revolver. He died from natural causes.

September 1965

Rose Cheramie*

Cheramie claimed to have knowledge of the assassination before 22 November 1963 and told of riding to Dallas from Miami with several Cubans who threw her out of the car. She later claimed that Ruby and Oswald were involved in a sexual liason. She was killed in a hit and run accident.

November 1965

Dorothy Kilgallen*

Highly respected newspaper columnist who was the only person to have a private interview with Ruby whilst he was in jail. Kilgallen pledged to 'break' the JFK case wide open. Before she could, however, she died from a barbituate overdose, the autopsy revealing that she had enough drugs in her system to kill ten men.

Mrs. Earl Smith*

A close friend to Dorothy Kilgallen, Smith died only two days after the columnist and may have kept some of Kilgallen's notes. Her cause of death remains unknown.

December 1965

William Whaley*

Whaley was the Dallas cab driver who drove Oswald to his rooming house in Oak Cliff within an hour of the assassination. Whaley died in an automobile accident, the first Dallas cabbie since 1937 to die in that manner.

1966

Judge Joe Brown

Presided over Jack Ruby's trial. He died from a heart attack.

January 1966

Earlene Roberts

Oswald's landlady at 1026 North Beckley who testified that Oswald rushed into his room shortly after Kennedy had been shot. Moments before Oswald left his room, a Dallas police car drew up outside the rooming house and sounded its horn twice before driving off. She stated that this happened sometime after one o'clock, not giving Oswald enough time to reach the Tippit murder scene on foot. Mrs Roberts died from a heart attack.

February 1966

Albert Bogard*

Dallas car salesman who said a man who gave his name as Oswald test drove a new car at high speeds just weeks before the assassination. When Bogard berated the man for driving so fast, he told Bogard that he might have to 'return to Russia' to buy a car. Oswald could not drive. Bogard's death was ruled a suicide.

June 1966

Capt. Frank Martin

Martin was a Dallas police captain who witnessed the Oswald slaying. He told the Warren Commission 'there's a lot to be said, but probably be better if I don't say it' and refused to testify before the Commission. He died of cancer.

August 1966

Lee Bowers, Jr.*

Bowers witnessed several suspicious cars in the parking lot behind the grassy knoll 30 minutes before the assassination. He also saw men behind a picket fence on the grassy knoll and saw a 'commotion' there at the time of the assassination. The patholgist stated that Bowers was in a state of 'strange, physical shock' at the time of his accident. Bowers was involved in a motor accident, though no other vehicles were involved.

September 1966

Marilyn "Delilah" Walle*

Hired by Jack Ruby as a dancer on the day of the assassination, Walle was shot dead by her husband after one month marriage. She told friends she was about to start and write a book about the JFK assassination.

October 1966

William Pitzer*

JFK autopsy photographer who described his duty as 'horrifying experience'. Gunshot, ruled suicide.

November 1966

Jimmy Levens

Fort Worth nightclub owner who hired Ruby employees. Levens died from natural causes.

James Worrell, Jr*

Worrell claimed to have heard a fourth shot in Dealey Plaza and then saw a man flee the rear of the Texas School Book Depository building immediately following the assassination. He died in a motor accident involving another car and a motor cycle.

Clarence Oliver

D.A. investigator who worked on the Jack Ruby case. Cause of death unknown.

December 1966

Hank Suydam

Life magazine official in charge of JFK stories. Death from heart attack.

The Garrison Inquiry 1966-69

1967

Leonard Pullin

Civilian Navy employee who helped film The Last Two Days, a film about the JFK assassination. Died in a one-car crash.

Jan 1967

Jack Ruby*

Dallas night club owner with Mafia connections (he was 'runner' for Al Capone as a young man). Lee Oswald's murderer. Ruby was also an acquaintance of David Ferrie. Ruby had been in a Dallas prison cell for three years when Jim Garrison's investigation became public knowledge. Garrison was about to subpoena Jack Ruby before he died from lung cancer. (Ruby told family he believed he was being injected with cancer cells, though this was never proven).

February 1967

Harold Russell*

Russell saw Tippit's killer running from the scene, but didn't identify him as Lee Oswald. Russell later told friends his life was in danger. Whilst at a party, Russell became agitated saying that he was going to be killed. The police were called and during the argument, Russell was struck by a police officer. Russell died later in hospital.

February 1967

David William Ferrie*

Former CIA pilot and acquaintance of Lee Oswald, Jack Ruby and Clay Shaw. Employee of W Guy Banister and New Orleans Mafia kingpin Carlos Marcello. Ferrie was Oswald's superior whilst

Oswald was a teenager serving in the Civil Air Patrol. This relationship had always been denied until a photograph was produced showing the two of them together. Ferrie is also believed to have managed Ruby's Carousel Club for a short period. A Ruby/Ferrie connection has always been denied. Several witnesses claim that Ferrie was with Oswald in the Carousel only days before the assassination.

At the time of his death, Ferrie was about to be arrested by Jim Garrison. Garrison always maintained that Ferrie was a possible getaway pilot for the actual assassins. David Ferrie died of a brain haemorrhage. Ferrie's apartment was strewn with empty pill containers, one being Proloid, a drug known to cause brain hemorrhage. His death was ruled a suicide and two separate typed, yet unsigned, suicide notes were found. Autopy photos reveal several contusions to his upper lip, perhaps caused by extreme pressure.

Eladio Del Vallé*

Anti-Castro Cuban associate of David Ferrie sought by Jim Garrison. Del Vallé was murdered in Miami the same hour as David Ferrie. He was attacked by several men and was killed by a gunshot wound to the chest after being axed several times in the head.

March 1967

Dr. Mary Sherman*

Ferrie associate working on cancer research. Died in fire.

January 1968

A. D. Bowie

Assistant Dallas D.A. who prosecuted Jack Ruby. Died from cancer.

April 1968

Hiram Ingram

Dallas Deputy Sheriff and close friend to Roger Craig (see below). Died from cancer.

May 1968

Dr. Nicholas Chetta

New Orleans Coroner who ruled on death of Ferrie. Chetta was to have been a key witness for the prosecution in the Clay Shaw trial, but died from heart attack before he could testify.

August 1968
Philip Geraci*
Friend of gay prostitute Perry Russo, who spoke of a Lee Oswald/Clay Shaw conversation. Russo was a prominent figure in the Garrison case. He died from electrocution.
January 1969
Henry Geraci*
Brother-in-law to coroner Chetta. Murdered.
January 1969
E. R. 'Buddy' Walthers*
Dallas Deputy Sheriff who was involved in Depository search and claimed to have found .45-cal. bullet in the grass on the south side of Elm Street, directly opposite the Grassy Knoll. There are photographs of this incident. Walthers also filed a report that Lee Harvey Oswald had attended 'Anti-Castro Meetings' at 3126 Harlandale Street, Dallas, in the weeks before the assassination. Walthers was shot dead by a felon.
1969
Charles Mentesana
Filmed a rifle other than Mannlicher-Carcano being taken from Depository within hours of the assassination. Mentesana died from a heart attack.
April 1969
Mary Bledsoe
Bledsoe was a neighbour to Lee Oswald and also knew David Ferrie. She died from natural causes.
June 1969
John Crawford*
Close friend to both Jack Ruby and Oswald's neighbour and co-worker Wesley Frazier. Died with four others when the plane Crawford was piloting crashed. The investigation into the crash later showed that Crawford and his passengers left on the trip in a hurry - their car keys were still in their cars and one woman left her purse on the front seat of her car.

July 1969

Rev. Clyde Johnson*

Scheduled to testify about the Clay Shaw/Oswald connection. Died from shotgun wounds.

1970

George McGann*

Underworld figure connected to Ruby friends; his wife, Beverly, took a film of the JFK assassination. Beverley was seen in other photographs taken of the assassination, though wasn't identified until many years later. The photos show her taking a film of the shooting and, from her position, must show the Grassy Knoll at the time of Kennedy's head shot. The film, though held by the US government, has never been publicly shown. McGann was murdered.

January 1970

Darrell W. Garner

The man arrested for shooting Warren Reynolds in 1964 but released following an alibi from Betty MacDonald. Garner died from a drugs overdose.

August 1970

Bill Decker

Dallas sheriff who saw a bullet hit street in front of JFK. Decker died from natural causes.

Abraham Zapruder

Zapruder took the most famous film of the JFK assassination, a film that became a clock for the shooting. He sold it to Time/Life for an undisclosed sum. The film, clearly showing JFK being hit by a bullet from his front right, thereby proving a conspiracy, was withheld from public viewing until 1975. Zapruder died from natural causes.

December 1970

Salvatore Granello*

Mobster linked to Teamsters boss Jimmy Hoffa, Mafia don Santos Trafficante and Fidel Castro assassination plots. Murdered.

Richard Randolph Carr

From his high vantage point on the Dallas County Government

Center building roof, Carr saw men running from behind the picket fence on the Grassy Knoll following the assassination and two men run from behind the Book depository and get into a Rambler station wagon. He also saw a man with a hat and glasses on the sixth floor of the Book Depository just before the assassination. Carr was never called to appear before the Wareen Commission. He was later attacked at home by two assailants. Carr killed one of them the other escaped but was never aprehended. No charges were brought against him for the death. The day before testifying for Jim Garrison, he found a bomb wired to his automobile. He was later stabbed to death.

1971

James Plumeri*

Mobster tied to mob/CIA assassination plots. Murdered.

Mar 1971

Clayton Fowler

Jack Ruby's chief defence attorney. Cause of death unknown.

April 1971

Gen.Charles Cabell*

The former CIA deputy director, sacked by Kennedy, was connected to anti-castro Cubans. He collapsed and died after a medical at Fort Myers.

<u>The Church Committee Investigation</u>

1972

Congressman Hale Boggs*

House majority leader and member of Warren Commission who began to publicly express doubts about the official findings, especially the 'single bullet theory' that the whole case against Oswald relied on. Boggs died in plane crash and his body was never recovered.

May 1972

J. Edgar Hoover*

FBI director who pushed "lone assassin" theory in the JFK assassination and vehemently denied Oswald's links with the FBI. Hoover, Director of the FBI for fifty years, died of a heart attack. No autopsy was performed.

September 1973

Thomas E. Davis*

Gun runner connected to both Ruby and the CIA. Died from elecrocution.

February 1974

J. A. Milteer*

Milteer was a prominent Miami right-winger who predicted JFK's death and the capture of a scapegoat months before the assassination. He appears in a photograph watching Kennedy's limousine as it approaches Dealy Plaza. He died from burns following a heater explosion, although it was reported that his wounds were healing.

1974

Dave Yaras*

Close friend to both Teamsters Union Boss Jimmy Hoffa and Jack Ruby. Murdered.

July 1974

Earl Warren

Earl Warren is said to have openly wept when President Johnson asked him to head the investigation into Kennedy's death. His reluctance to head the investigation, however, has never been fully explained. He died from heart failure.

Aug 1974

Clay Shaw*

Following the mysterious deaths of Jack Ruby and David Ferrie, Shaw became the prime suspect in the Garrison case and was charged with conspiring to murder president John F Kennedy. Garrison, whilst convincing the jury that the CIA were somehow involved in the assassination, could not, however, prove that Shaw was a contract agent for the CIA and he was subsequently aquitted. Shaw is thought to be a CIA contact with David Ferrie and Lee Harvey Oswald. Ferrie, Shaw and Oswald were seen together on many occasions in New Orleans during the summer of 1963. In 1979, ten years after Shaw's trial, it was revealed that Shaw had, indeed, been a contract agent for the CIA. Shaw died from cancer. No autopsy was performed.

Earle Cabell

Mayor of Dallas on 11/22/63, whose brother, Gen. Charles Cabell, was fired from the CIA by JFK, died from natural causes.

June 1975

Sam Giancana*

The Chicago Mafia boss was about to testify about CIA/Mafia death plots against Fidel Castro to a Senate committee. Only days before he was to speak, Giancana was shot five times in the face, his murderer was never apprehended.

1975

Clyde Tolson

J. Edgar Hoover's assistant and, some say, lover, died from natural causes.

July 1975

Allan Sweatt

Dallas Deputy Sheriff, involved in investigating Oswald, died from natural causes.

August 1975

Roger D Craig*

Dallas Police Captain and Dallas Police Officer of the Year in 1962, Craig criticised the handling of the JFK case by the Dallas authorities and the Government. He was forced out of the Dallas Police Department and went onto to help the Garrison enquiry in 1968. Forced off the road by a truck, shot and wounded on several separate occasions, Craig allegedly shot himself in the head.

December 1975

Gen. Earl Wheeler

Contact between JFK and CIA, cause of death unknown.

1976

Ralph Paul

Paul was Ruby's business partner and was connected with major crime figures at the time of the assassination. Reportly died from a heart attack.

April 1976

James Chaney

Chaney was the Dallas motorcycle officer riding to JFK's right rear, thereby being the nearest person to JFK, apart from those in the limousine, who testified that JFK had been "struck in the face" with the final bullet. Chaney died from a heart attack.

Dr. Charles Gregory

Governor John Connally's physician. He died from a heart attack.

June 1976

William Harvey*

CIA coordinator for CIA/Mafia assassination plans against Fidel Castro, died from complications of heart surgery.

John Roselli*

Mobster, acquaintance of Carlos Marchello and Santos Trafficante, who testified to Senate committee. Roselli was stabbed to death, cut up and stuffed in a metal drum. He was found there eleven months after he disappeared.

January 1977

William Pawley*

Former Brazilian ambassador connected to anti-Castro Cubans and organised crime figures. He died after sustaining a gunshot which was ruled a suicide.

March 1977

George DeMohrenschildt*

Close friend to both Oswald and Bouvier families (Jackie Kennedy's parents), a former oil man with links to the intelligence community. Many investigators believe that DeMohrenschildt was Oswald's CIA 'babysitter'. DeMohrenschildt always claimed that Oswald was innocent and that the alleged assassin admired Kennedy. He died the day before he was due to testify before the House Select Commititee on Assassinations from a shotgun wound to the head. Ruled a suicide.

Carlos Prio Soccaras*

Former Cuban president and money man for anti-Castro Cubans. He died from a gunshot wound which was ruled a suicide.

March 1977
Paul Raigorodsky
Business friend of George DeMohrenschildt and wealthy oilman, died from natural causes.
May 1977
Lou Staples*
Dallas radio talk show host who told friends that he would break the JFK assassination case wide open. He later died from a gunshot to the head. It was ruled a suicide.
June 1977
Louis Nichols
Former number-three man in Hoover's FBI, where he worked on the JFK investigation in 1964. He died from a heart attack.
August 1977
Alan Belmont
FBI official who testified before the Warren Commission in 1964. Died following a 'long illness'.
James Cadigan
FBI document expert who testified before the Warren Commission in 1964. He died following a fall in his home.
Joseph C. Ayres*
Chief steward on JFK's Air Force One died following a shooting accident.
Francis G Powers*
U-2 pilot downed over Soviet Union in 1960, who blamed Oswald for passing on secrets of U2 flights to Soviet Officials. He died in a helicopter crash after he reportedly ran out of fuel.
September 1977
Kenneth O'Donnell
JFK's closest aide during Kennedy administration, died of natural causes.
October 1977
Donald Kaylor
FBI fingerprint chemist. Died following a heart attack.

J. M. English

Former head of FBI Forensic Sciences Laboratory. Died following a heart attack.

November 1977

William Sullivan*

Former number-three man in FBI, headed Division 5, counterespionage and domestic intelligence. Died from a gunshot wound in a freak hunting accident.

1978

C. L. "Lummie" Lewis

Dallas Deputy Sheriff who arrested Mafia man Eugene Hale Braden in Dealey Plaza following the assassination. Lewis died from natural causes.

September 1978

Garland Slack

Slack was the man who said Lee Harvey Oswald fired at his target at a rifle range shortly before the JFK assassination. When "Oswald" was confronted by Slack for shooting at his target, the man said he thought he was shooting at "that son of a bitch Kennedy". The Warren Commission never placed Oswald at any firing ranges. Slack's cause of death is unknown.

January 1979

Billy Lovelady

Texas Schoolbook Depository employee said to be the 'man in the doorway' in Bill Altgens' AP photograph. Many investigators believe the 'man in the doorway' is, in fact, Oswald and therefore could not be shooting at Kennedy. Lovelady bears such an uncanny resemblance to Oswald that Lovelady's own wife shouted to him one day at the Book Depository, thinking him to be her husband. Lovelady died of complications following a heart attack.

June 1980

Jesse Curry

Dallas Police Chief at the time of the assassination. Curry stated that he could not place Oswald in the snipers nest at the time of the shooting. Curry died from a heart attack.

Dr. John Holbrook
Dallas Psychiatrist who testified that Jack Ruby was not insane. Died from a suspected heart attack, but pills and notes were found.

January 1981
Marguerite Oswald
Mother of Lee Harvey Oswald. Campaigned from day one that her son was innocent of the charges against him. Ridiculed and abused following the assassination, she maintained that Oswald had been working for the CIA whilst in the Soviet Union. Mrs Oswald died of cancer.

October 1981
Frank Watts
Chief felony prosecutor for Dallas D.A. Died from natural causes.

Jan 1982
Peter Gregory
Original translator for Marina Oswald and Secret Service, died from natural causes.

May 1982
Dr. James Weston
Pathologist allowed to see JFK autopsy material for HSCA. Died while jogging and ruled death by natural causes.

August 1982
Will H. Griffin
FBI agent who reportedly said Lee Oswald was 'definitely' an FBI informant. Griffin died from cancer.

October 1982
W. Marvin Gheesling
FBI official who helped supervise JFK investigation. Died from natural causes.

March 1984
Roy Kellerman
Secret Service agent in charge of JFK limousine, sat directly in front of Govenor John Connally during the shooting. Cause of death unknown.

1988

Jim Hicks

Jim Garrison stated that he believed Hicks to be a radio co-ordinator in Dealey Plaza at the time of the assassination. Hicks appears in several photographs before, during and after the shooting. After testifying to Garrison in 1968, Hicks was beaten up and held in a mental institution. In 1988, only days after his release, he was murdered.

No doubt this list is inaccurate and certainly incomplete.

Bibliography

Anson, Robert Sam. *'They've Killed The President!" The Search for the Murderers of John F Kennedy.* Bantam Books, Inc., 666 Fifth Avenue, New York, 10019, U.S.A.

Berkley, Edmund C., Editor. *People and the Pursuit of Truth.* May 1975-September 1978. 815 Washington Street, Newtonville, Mass., 02160, U.S.A.

Blumenthal, Sid and Yazijan, Harvey, Edited by. *Government By Gunplay: Assassination Conspiracy Theories From Dallas to Watergate.* The New American Library, 1301 Avenue of the Americas, New York, N. Y. 10019, U.S.A.

Brewer, Milton E. *The Garrison Case, A Study in the Abuse of Power.* Clarkson N. Potter, Inc. New York.

Buchanan, Thomas C. *Who Killed Kennedy?* Putnam, New York, N.Y.

Cockburn, Alex. *Echoes of Dallas : The JFK Assassination Fifteen Years Later.* Magill Monthly, 14 Merrion Row, Dublin 2.

Cutler, Robert B. *The Flight of C.E. 399 - Evidence of Conspiracy.* Box 1465, Manchester, MA 01944.

- *Seventy Six Seconds in Dealy Plaza.* Ibid.
- *Mr. Chairman : Evidence of Conspiracy.* Ibid.
- *The Day of the Umbrella Man.* Ibid.

Eddowes, Michael. *November 22 : How They Killed Kennedy.* Neville Spearman Ltd., London.

- *The Oswald File.* Clarkson N. Potter, New York, N.Y.

Evica, George Michael. *And We Are All Mortal: New Evidence and Analysis in the Assassination of John F. Kennedy.* University of Hartford, 200 Bloomfield Avenue West Hartford, Conn., 06117, U.S.A.

Epstein, Edward, J. *Inquest : The Warren Commission and the Establishment of Truth.* Bantam Books, Inc., 625 Madison Avenue, New York, N.Y. 10022.

- *Legend: The Secret World of Lee Harvey Oswald.* McGraw Hill, New York.

Fleming, Glenn B. *Patsy.* Unpublished manuscript, 1976.

- *The Oswald Papers : Rumours and Research.* Unpublished manuscript, 1985.

- *S-172 : Lee Harvey Oswald's Links to Intelligence Agencies.* Privately Published 1998.

- Roger Dean Craig : *A Man in History.* Privately Published 1999.

Flint, Larry. *JFK Murder Solved.* L.A. Free Press, Special Report no. 1, Press West, Inc., 5850 Hollywood Blvd., Los Angeles, CA.

- *Garrison Charges that Pentagon Planned JFK Killing.* December 22 1972. Ibid.

Ford, Gerald R., with Stiles John R., *Portrait of the Assassin.* Simon & Schuster, New York, N.Y.

Fox, Sylvan. *The Unanswered Questions about President Kennedy's Assassination.* Award Books, New York, U.S.A.

Garrison, Jim. *A Heritage of Stone.* Berkley Publishing Corporation, 200 Madison avenue, New York N.Y. 10016.

Bibliography

Glassner, Barry. *Revisiting the Great American Tragedies : From Kennedy to Kent State.* In Touch Magazine, November 1974.

Goldberg, Jeff. *Waiting For Justice.* Inquiry Magazine, 1979.

- and Yazijian, Harvey. *The Death of 'Crazy Billy' Sullivan.* New Times Magazine Special Report, 24th July, 1978.

Groden, Robert J. *The Killing of a President.*Bloomsbury, 1993.

- *The Search for Lee Harvey Oswald.*Bloomsbury, 1995.

Gunn, Nerin E. *Red Roses from Texas.* 1964.

Hale, Hazel. *Oswald.* (Unpublished Manuscript) 1978.

Hepburn, James (pseudonym). *Farewell America.* Frontiers Publishing Company, Vaduz, Liechtenstein. 1968.

Irwin, Harry. *JFK Assassination Forum.* (Newsletter). Harry Irwin, 32 Ravensdene Crescent, Ravenhill, Belfast BT6 0DB, Northern Ireland. 1975-1981.

Jenkins, David. *116 for 1.* Time Out, Time Out Limited, 374 Grays Inn Road, London WC1X 8BB. 1973.

Jones, Penn jnr. *Forgive My Grief Volumes 1, 2, 3 and 4.* P.O. Box 1140, Midlothian, Texas, U.S.A. 1965-67

Joesten, Joachim. *Oswald, Assassin or Fall Guy?* Marzani & Munsell Publishers Inc., New York, N.Y.

- *Oswald, The Truth.* Peter Dawney, London. 1967.

- *Marina Oswald.* Ibid.

Kantor, Seth. *Who Was Jack Ruby?* Everest House, New York, N.Y., U.S..A. 1978

Kelley, Kit. People Weekly, February 29th, 1988. Time & Life Building, Rockefeller Center, New York, N.Y. 10020.

Kirkwood, James. *American Grotesque: An Account of the Clay Shaw - Jim Garrison Affair in New Orleans.* Simon and Schuster, New York, U.S.A. 1969.

Kruger, Henrik. *The Great Heroin Coup : Drugs, Intelligence & International Fascism.* South End Press, Box 68 Astor Station, Boston, MA 02123.

Lane, Mark. *Rush To Judgment.* Holt, Rinehart & Wilson, New York. 1966.

- *A Citizen's Dissent.* Fawcett World Library, 67 West 44th Street, New York, N. Y., 10036, U.S.A. 1968.

Life, July 10th, 1964. Time Inc., 540 N. Michigan Av., Chicago, Illinois 60611, U.S.A.

- November 24th, 1967. Ibid.

Latzen, Morris S. *The Kennedy Assassination : The Full Story.* Confidential Detective Yearbook 1964, Sterling House, Inc., 260 Park Avenue South, New York, N. Y., 10010.

Lime, Vic and Ramsey, Robin. *Cover-ups & Conspiracies : A Unique Investigation Into the Dark Side of the Kennedy Legend.* Revelations Magazine, P.O. Box 150, London E5 0LU.

Lutz, Tom. *Tracking Down Kennedy's Killers.* Newsreal, July 1977. Newsreal Series, P.O. Box 147, Morton Grove, Ill. 60053.

- Newsreal, October 1977. Ibid.

MacFarlane, Ian. *Proof of Conspiracy In the assassination of President Kennedy.* Book Distributors, Australia. 1975.

Manchester, William. *The Death of a President: November 20 - 25, 1963.* Harper & Row, New York, N.Y. 1968.

McDonald, Hugh and Moore, Robin. *L.B.J. and the J.F.K. Conspiracy.* Condor Publishing Company Inc., 29 East Main Street, Westport, Connecticut 06880.

MacMillan, Priscilla Johnson. *Marina and Lee.* Harper & Row. 1977.

Meagher, Sylvia. *Accessories After The Fact: The Warren Commission, The Authorities and The Report.* Vintage Books, U.S.A.

Moldea, Dan E. *The Hoffa Wars, Teamsters, Rebels, Politicians and the Mob.* Paddington Press, U.S.A. 1978.

- *Who Killed Jimmy Hoffa and Why.* Playboy, November 1978.

Morrow, Robert D. *Betrayal, A Reconstruction of Certain Clandestine Events from the Bay of Pigs to the Assassination of John F. Kennedy.* Warner Books Inc., 75 Rockefeller Plaza, New York, N.Y. 10019.

Noyes, Peter. *Legacy of Doubt.* Pinnacle Books, New York, N.Y.

Norden, Eric. *Jim Garrison : A Candid Conversation with the Embattled District Attorney of New Orleans.* Playboy, October 1967.HMH Publishing, Michigan Avenue, Chicago, Ill, U.S.A.

- *High Noon in Dallas.* Lords, The Gentleman's Companion, (Summer 1969) Lords Magazine Ltd., 2 Bramber Road, London W14.

Oglesby, Carl. *The Yankee and Cowboy War : Conspiracies from Dallas to Watergate and Beyond.* Berkley Publishing Corporation, 200 Madison Avenue, New York, N.Y. U.S.A.

O'Toole, George. *The Assassination Tapes : An Electronic Probe into the Murder of John F Kennedy and the Dallas Cover-up.* Penthouse Press, New York, N. Y.

Prouty, Fletcher L. *An Introduction to the Assassination Business.* Gallery. Gallery, September 1975. Montcalm Publishing Corporation, 99 Park Avenue, New York, N.Y. 10016.

- *The Guns of Dallas*, Gallery, October 1975. Ibid.

-*The Guns of Dallas : Update*. Gallery, May 1976. Ibid.

Popkin, Richard H. *The Second Oswald*. Avon Library-New York Review Books, New York, U.S.A.

Ramsey, Robin. *The Jemstone File*. International times, 97A Talbot Road, London W11.

Roffman, Howard. *Presumed Guilty*. Associated University Presses, Inc. Cranbury, New Jersey 08512, U.S.A. 1976.

Sahl, Mort. *Heartland*. Harcourt Brace and Jovanovich. New York and London. 1977.

Sauvage, Leo. *The Oswald Affair : An Examination of the Contradictions and Omissions of the Warren Report*. World Publishing Co., Cleveland.

Scally, Christopher. *"So near ... and yet so far." The House Select Committee on Assassinations' Investigations into the Murder of President John F. Kennedy*. Privately published, Essex. 1981.

Scott, Peter Dale, with Hoch, Paul and Stetler, Russell. *The Assassinations : Dallas and Beyond - A Guide to Cover-ups and Investigations*. Pelican Books, 625 Madison Avenue, New York, N. Y.

Shaw, J. Gary, and Harris, Larry R. *Cover-up; The Governmental Conspiracy to Conceal the Facts about the Public Execution of John Kennedy*. Cleburne, Texas. (Available from the Author). 1975.

Sloan, Bill. *The Other Assassin*. Tudor Publishing, Inc., 276 Fifth Avenue, New York, N. Y. 10001.

Sneed, Larry A. Three Forks Press, PO Box 823461, Dallas, Texas. 1998

Sprague, Richard E. *The Assassination of John F. Kennedy : The Application of Computers to the Photographic Evidence.*

Computers and Automation, May 1970.

- *The Taking of America 1-2-3.* (Privately Published) 1976.

Stafford, Jean. *A Mother In History: Mrs. Marguerite Oswald.* Farrar, Strauss and Giroux, New York. 1965.

Stark, Andrew. *The CIA's Secret Weapons Systems.* Gallery, June 1978. Montcalm Publishing Corporation, 99 Park Avenue, New York, N.Y. 10016.

Summers, Anthony. *Conspiracy: Who Killed President Kennedy?* Fontana Paperbacks, U.K. 1978.

- *The Kennedy Cover-up.* The Listener, 9th March,1978. Published by the BBC.

Staff Writer. *Where is it now?* Sunday Express Magazine, 6th November 1983. Express Newspapers p.l.c., Fleet Street, London EC4P 4JT.

William Shawcross. *The Day of the Conspirator.* Sunday Times Magazine, July 27th, 1975, Times Newspapers Ltd., P.O. Box 7, New Printing House Square, Gray's Inn Road, London WC1X 8EZ.

Thompson, Josiah. *Six Seconds in Dallas : A Microstudy of the Kennedy Assassination.* Bernard Geiss, New York, N.Y.

Truby, David J. *Mystery of the Umbrella Man.* The Globe, 29th July, 1980.

Turner, William W. *The Garrison Commission on the Assassination of President Kennedy.* Ramparts, January 1968. 301 Broadway, San Francisco, California 94133, U.S.A.

United States Government Printing Office, Washington D. C.*The President's Commission on the Assassination of President Kennedy: REPORT and 26 Volume's of Evidence.*

Various. *The JFK Assassination.* Gallery, Special Report, July 1979. Montcalm Publishing Corporation, 99 Park Avenue,

New York, N.Y. 10016.

Various. *The Death of Marilyn Monroe.* Scandal (Part 2). Orbis Publishing Ltd., Griffin House, 161 Hammersmith Road, London W6 8SD.

Weisberg, Harold. *Post Mortem.* Harold Weisberg, Route 12, Old Receiver Road, Frederick, Md, 21701, U.S.A.

- *Whitewash 1 : The Report on the Warren Report.* Ibid.

- *Whitewash 2 : The FBI - Secret Service Cover-up.* Ibid.

- *Photographic Whitewash : Suppressed Kennedy Assassination Pictures.* Ibid.

- *Whitewash 4 : JFK Assassination Transcript.* Ibid.

- *Oswald In New Orleans - Case for Conspiracy with the CIA.* Canyon Books, New York, N. Y.